SCHOLASTIC

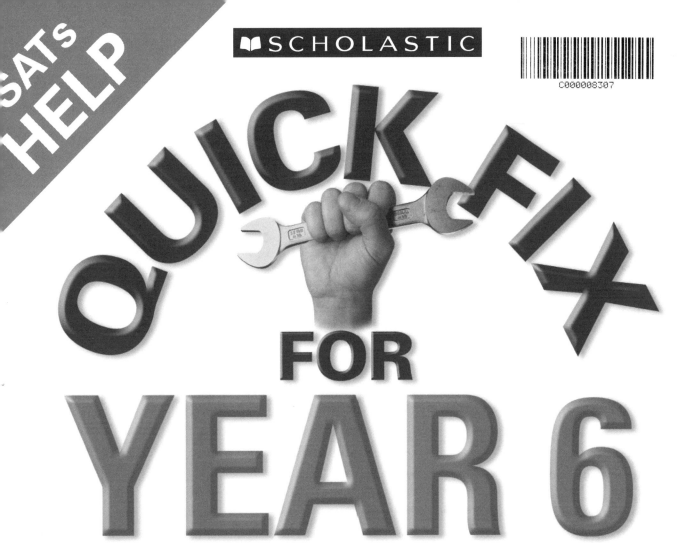

QUICK FIX

FOR

YEAR 6

MATHS

Stress-busting SATs solutions

Techniques for top marks

Follows the revised PNS Framework

Richard Cooper

CREDITS

Author
Richard Cooper

Editors
Dodi Beardshaw
Ruth Burns
Sara Wiegand

Series Designer
Anna Oliwa

Designer
Mike Brain Graphic
Design Limited, Oxford

Illustrations
Beverly Curl
Garry Davies

Acknowlegements
Extracts from the Primary National Strategy's *Primary Framework for Mathematics* © 2006 Crown copyright and other Crown copyright material. Reproduced under the terms of the Click Use Licence.

Text © Richard Cooper
© 2007 Scholastic Ltd

Designed using Adobe InDesign

Published by Scholastic Ltd
Villiers House
Clarendon Avenue
Leamington Spa
Warwickshire CV32 5PR
www.scholastic.co.uk

Printed by Bell and Bain Ltd.

1 2 3 4 5 6 7 8 9   7 8 9 0 1 2 3 4 5 6

British Library Cataloguing-in-Publication Data
A catalogue record for this book is available from the British Library.

ISBN 978-0439-94569-1

CONTENTS

INTRODUCTION

Quick Fix for Year 6 Maths is designed to support teachers in the build-up to the Year 6 SATs maths tasks. It provides the tools to organise and run a detailed, structured programme of 'booster classes'. These are extra-curricular classes run at lunchtimes or after school, giving the Year 6 pupils extra tuition and a chance to revise key objectives. Pupils who successfully complete the programme should go on to achieve a Level 4 or above.

The programme includes:

■ 20 easy-to-follow photocopiable lesson plans with accompanying worksheets;

■ Lessons that are designed to make life as easy as possible for the teacher. Minimal preparation is required, yet all the key objectives are covered to achieve a Level 4;

■ Two sample tests – one at a SATs Level 3 standard and one at Level 4;

■ A mental maths test; similar to the one the pupils will take in their SATs;

■ Activities that will stretch the more able pupils;

■ A pre-written permission letter to parents;

■ A reward certificate for attendance and achievement;

■ A 12-week programme for the build-up to the SATs – teachers can copy this and use it as a medium-term planning sheet;

■ A student progress chart for pupils to fill in and monitor their achievements as they progress through the booster lessons;

■ A photocopiable sheet of key facts which the pupils can put in their folders or the teacher can place on the wall;

■ Tips and advice for pupils on how to revise and how to plan their revision time;

■ Hints and tips for success in every lesson;

■ Advice on exam technique – before and during the SATs;

■ Full answers to all the sample questions.

HOW TO USE THIS BOOK

In order to make the book easy to use, all the lessons follow the same format:

■ What you need – minimal equipment, but nothing that can't be found in most classrooms;

■ Introduction – a quick and easy start to the lesson;

■ Whole class teaching – key explanations led by the teacher;

■ Main teaching points – three key points for the pupils to learn.

■ Review – how to finish the session;

■ Homework ideas – using existing resources found at school;

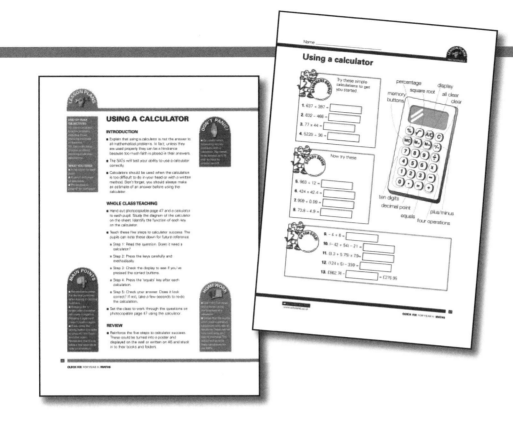

Each lesson is designed to last 20–25 minutes which should enable it to fit within lunch breaks at most schools;

Each worksheet is differentiated. They are divided into three sections: Beginner's Bronze, Steady Silver and Go for Gold! The bronze section will be in the Level 3 range, the silver in the Level 3/4 range and the gold at Levels 4/5. Steady success at silver level will give a good indication of progress for each child. The lessons and worksheets are designed to be photocopied at short notice. The teacher could deliver the lesson with the lesson plan in one hand or strategically placed on the desk!

There are a number of pages which can be photocopied and handed out to pupils for future reference or to take home and study.

ASSESSING PUPILS' WORK

The sample tests can be administered before or after the booster programme. They can be used as an indication of ability beforehand to enable the teacher to identify gaps in knowledge or areas of strength. Alternatively, after the 20 lessons the tests could give an indication of how much progress has been made over the course of the programme. Any pupils who are comfortable with the Level 4 test should achieve that level or higher when it comes to the SATs in May.

A GUIDE TO RUNNING BOOSTER LESSONS

In order to give pupils a chance to properly prepare for the SATs it is important to plan the revision period well. Schools differ over when to start revising but the beginning of the Spring Term is seen by many to be ideal.

Here is a 'ten steps to success' guide to get your Year 6 booster lessons up and running quickly and efficiently.

1. Discuss with your pupils what the SATs are and when they will be taking them (May). Try to instil a sense of team spirit and collective pride. You don't want your pupils to worry about doing badly but you do want them to worry about doing well. A common misconception amongst Year 6 pupils is that the levels they achieve in the tests will determine their 'choice' of secondary school. This is a fear that should be laid to rest. For the pupils, the SATs should be seen as a chance to prove to themselves, their parents and the school what they have learnt. Away from the classroom, the pressure is certainly on teachers and headteachers for the Year 6 students to attain the highest possible levels, so taking a responsible and dedicated approach to revision is highly recommended.

2. Introduce the idea of booster lessons to the pupils. This may not seem like an attractive proposition to some – usually the ones who need them the most! You really need that 'pulling together' spirit at the beginning, so it's a good idea to get off to a good start and sell them the idea. You could discuss with the headteacher (who will be very keen to get the best from the pupils) the idea of offering some sort of reward for 100% attendance at booster lessons. This could be as a group and/or as individuals. Ideas for rewards include class trips after the SATs (a game of rounders and a picnic in the park doesn't cost very much), book/music tokens or the promise of a day spent playing organised sports tournaments in the playground (see the PE coordinator, if need be).

3. Inform the rest of the staff as soon as possible. Raise the topic of booster lessons at the next staff meeting and rally some support to help you run them. The three core subject coordinators and members of the senior management team should certainly be involved, but any offers of help from elsewhere would come in very handy. Again, your headteacher should support you here.

4. Timetable the booster lessons so everyone (teachers and pupils) will know when they are taking place. Highlight the available after-school and lunchtime sessions. Try to avoid clashing with popular extra-curricular events such as football club – remember, you need the pupils on side!

5. Aim for the same level of commitment from the Year 6 parents. They should welcome the idea but it is important they support the school by offering incentives at home as well as ensuring there is a quiet place to work (away from distractions like younger siblings and TV) and encouraging the completion of homework. Many schools arrange a 'SATs information evening' when the parents are invited in to ask questions about the tests and raise any concerns. If your headteacher has not arranged this, then ask if it is a possibility. You can photocopy the permission letter on page 8 or write your own.

6. Gather the necessary resources. Your school will have received funds for the purpose of revision, so there should not be a problem with pens, pencils, books and folders. Also, you don't want to waste valuable booster time searching for calculators or retrieving Maths equipment loaned to other classes.

7. Draw up a register of attendance for each booster class. You can photocopy the one on page 9 or produce your own.

8. Start the booster lessons with the 'How to revise' lesson (see page 12) and ensure each pupil has filled in their revision timetable. A photocopiable template for this can be found on page 14.

9. Establish with the pupils any rewards which are to be given once the booster lessons and SATs are over, and lay down the ground rules and expectations.

10. After the first booster lesson (How to revise) ask your headteacher to hold a special assembly to praise the Year 6 students for their commitment, ability and work ethic. They should feel like the 'big kids' of the school and will respond to the notion of providing an example to the younger children. Remember, once they are in Year 7 they will revert to being the 'babies' of their new school, so let them enjoy their status while it lasts!

LETTER TO PARENTS

Dear Parents/Carers,

As you are probably aware, all Year 6 pupils will be taking the Key Stage 2 National Tests for English, Maths and Science in May. These are generally known as SATs and will provide an indication of your child's attainment at the end of their primary school career. We are keen for our pupils to show the best they can do, so in addition to their normal timetable we have organised extra classes known as 'booster lessons'. These will give the pupils a chance to revise the work they have covered over the last three years and hopefully identify and address any gaps in knowledge.

Booster lessons will be taking place during lunch breaks and after school and it would be of great benefit to your child if they could attend as many sessions as possible.

Here is the timetable for these booster lessons, which start on _____ and will run for _____ weeks.

	Monday	Tuesday	Wednesday	Thursday	Friday	After school/ Lunchtime
English						
Math						
Science						

The booster lessons after school will start at _____ pm and finish at _____ pm. Please let us know what arrangements you will be making for your child to get home after these lessons by completing and returning the form below.

With best wishes

Year 6 Teacher(s)

☐ I give permission for my child to attend booster lessons.

☐ I will arrange for my child to be collected following after-school booster lessons.

☐ My child will be allowed to make their own way home following after-school booster lessons.

Signed _____ (Parent/Carer)

Pupil name _____ Class _____

Please return this form to your child's Year 6 teacher by _____

BOOSTER LESSON ATTENDANCE REGISTER

Subject _____ Teacher in charge _____

Name/Week	1	2	3	4	5	6	7	8	9	10	11	Permission slip	Getting home

QUICK FIX FOR YEAR 6: MATHS

OBJECTIVES CHART

The following chart details the framework objectives covered in each booster lesson.

QUICK FIX LESSON	FRAMEWORK OBJECTIVES
Place value (pages 34–35)	**Y5:** Explain what each digit represents in whole numbers
Ordering decimals (pages 36–37)	**Y5:** Explain what each digit represents in decimals with up to two places, and partition, round and order these numbers **Y6:** Use decimal notation for tenths, hundredths and thousandths; partition, round and order decimals with up to three places, and position them on a number line
A written method for addition (pages 38–39)	**Y5:** Use efficient written methods to add and subtract whole numbers and decimals with up to two places
A written method for subtraction (pages 40–41)	**Y5:** Use efficient written methods to add and subtract whole numbers and decimals with up to two places
A written method for multiplication (pages 42–43)	**Y5:** Refine and use efficient written methods to multiply HTU x U, TU x TU, U.t x U **Y6:** Use efficient written methods to multiply integers and decimals by a one-digit integer, and to multiply two-digit and three-digit integers by a two-digit integer
A written method for division (pages 44–45)	**Y4:** Develop and use written methods to record, support and explain division of two-digit numbers by a one-digit number, including division with remainders **Y5:** Refine and use efficient written methods to divide HTU ÷ U **Y6** progression to **Y7:** Extend division to dividing three-digit integers by a two-digit integer
Using a calculator (pages 46–47)	**Y5:** Use a calculator to solve problems, including those involving decimals or fractions **Y6:** Use a calculator to solve problems involving multi-step calculations
Checking your answers (pages 48–49)	**Y5:** Use knowledge of rounding, place value, number facts and inverse operations to estimate and check calculations **Y6:** Use approximations, inverse operations and tests of divisibility to estimate and check results
Fractions and percentages of quantities (pages 50–51)	**Y5/6:** Find fractions using division and percentages of numbers and quantities **Y6:** Find equivalent percentages, decimals and fractions
Factors, multiples and primes (pages 52–53)	**Y5:** Identify pairs of factors of two-digit whole numbers and find common multiples **Y6:** Recognise that prime numbers have only two factors and identify prime numbers less than 100; find the prime factors of two-digit numbers

Coordinates in the first quadrant (pages 54–55)	**Y5:** Read and plot coordinates in the first quadrant **Y6:** Use coordinates in the first quadrant to draw, locate and complete shapes that meet given properties
Reflective symmetry (pages 56–57)	**Y5:** Complete patterns with up to two lines of symmetry; draw the position of a shape after a reflection **Y6:** Visualise and draw on grids of different types where a shape will be after reflection
Drawing and measuring lines (pages 58–59)	**Y5:** Draw and measure lines to the nearest millimetre
Perimeter (pages 60–61)	**Y5:** Measure and calculate the perimeter of regular and irregular polygons **Y6:** Calculate the perimeter of rectilinear shapes
Finding the area of rectangles (pages 62–63)	**Y4:** Find the area of rectilinear shapes drawn on a grid by counting squares **Y5:** Use the formula for the area of a rectangle to calculate a rectangle's area **Y6:** Calculate the area of rectilinear shapes
Angles (pages 64–65)	**Y4:** Know that angles are measured in degrees and that one whole turn is 360 degrees; compare and order angles less than 180 degrees **Y5:** Estimate, draw and measure acute and obtuse angles using an angle measurer or protractor to a suitable degree of accuracy **Y6:** Estimate angles, and use a protractor to measure and draw them, on their own and in shapes; calculate angles in a triangle or around a point **Y6/7:** Know the sum of angles on a straight line, in a triangle and at a point, and recognise vertically opposite angles
Frequency tables (pages 66–67)	**Y5:** Construct frequency tables to represent the frequencies of events **Y6:** Solve problems by collecting, selecting, processing, presenting and interpreting data
Multi-step problems (pages 68–69)	**Y6:** Solve multi-step problems and problems involving fractions, decimals and percentages; choose and use appropriate calculation strategies at each stage, including calculator use
Number patterns (pages 70–71)	**Y5:** Explore patterns, properties and relationships and propose a general statement involving numbers or shapes **Y6:** Represent and interpret sequences, patterns and relationships involving numbers and shapes; suggest and test hypotheses
Solving problems (pages 72–73)	**Y5:** Represent a puzzle or problem by identifying and recording the information or calculations needed to solve it; find possible solutions and confirm them in the context of the problem **Y6:** Tabulate systematically the information in a problem or puzzle; identify and record the steps or calculations needed to solve it, using symbols where appropriate; interpret solutions in the original context and check their accuracy Explain reasoning and conclusions, using words, symbols or diagrams as appropriate

HOW TO REVISE

You will need a copy of the revision timetable example (page 13) and the blank version (page 14) for each pupil.

INTRODUCTION

■ Inform the pupils about your plans for them over the coming weeks. Tell them who will be teaching them, where they will be taught and when.

■ Establish your expectations from the start. Regular attendance and cooperative behaviour should be the minimum requirements from all pupils coming to the booster classes.

■ Explain to the pupils that this first session is to help them organise themselves and prepare properly by establishing a revision routine and timetable.

■ Tell the pupils that revision will reinforce learning and fill any gaps in knowledge. They shouldn't be tackling concepts which are completely alien, but if pupils have missed certain topics through lengthy absences, this is their (and your) chance to rectify these points.

WHOLE CLASS TEACHING

■ Discuss suitable places to work at home. Somewhere quiet where you are unlikely to be disturbed and somewhere you can keep your books and equipment laid out is ideal – for example, a desk in your bedroom. In front of the telly is not ideal!

■ Discuss when to work. 'Little and often' should be the tactic here. Three 15-minute sessions throughout the day can be more beneficial than an hour slumped over a text book before bed.

■ Discuss what to work on. Explain that the whole group will be working on a prepared plan of action.

■ Hand out a copy of the example revision timetable on page 13 and discuss with the group any issues that may arise.

■ Hand out a copy of the blank revision timetable on page 14 for each pupil to fill in themselves.

■ Pupils need to keep the timetables somewhere easily accessible. If they have a booster class folder, they could attach it to the inside cover.

REVIEW

■ The pupils could share their ideas on mixing leisure and revision time.

■ You may want to encourage your pupils to pair up as 'revision buddies'. They could support each other out of class by doing homework together.

EXAMPLE REVISION TIMETABLE

	Monday	Tuesday	Wednesday	Thursday	Friday	Saturday	Sunday
7.00am	Key facts – Maths 10 mins	Key facts – Science 10 mins	Key facts – English 10 mins	Key facts – Maths 10 mins	Key facts – Science 10 mins	Key facts – English 10 mins	Sleep
8.00am							Sleep
9.00am	Numeracy hour	Numeracy hour	Numeracy hour	Numeracy hour	Numeracy hour		
10.00am	Literacy hour	Literacy hour	Literacy hour	Literacy hour	Literacy hour	Play football	Swimming
11.00am		Science		Science			
12.00pm		12.30 – Science booster	12.30 – Maths booster	12.30 – Science booster	12.30 – English booster		
1.00pm							Sunday lunch
2.00pm		PE			Art class	Shopping	Walk the dog
3.00pm	3.30 – Maths booster		3.30 – English booster				
4.00pm				Guitar lesson		Bike ride	
5.00pm							English homework
6.00pm	Maths homework	Science homework	English homework	Maths homework	Science homework	Cinema	TV
7.00pm	Spellings		Spellings		Maths vocabulary		
8.00pm	Read/bed	Read/bed	Read/bed	Read/bed	Read/bed		Read/bed

■SCHOLASTIC
www.scholastic.co.uk

Name _____

REVISION TIMETABLE

	7.00am	8.00am	9.00am	10.00am	11.00am	12.00pm	1.00pm	2.00pm	3.00pm	4.00pm	5.00pm	6.00pm	7.00pm	8.00pm
Monday														
Tuesday														
Wednesday														
Thursday														
Friday														
Saturday														
Sunday														

Name _____

STUDENT PROGRESS CHART

QUICK FIX LESSON	BRONZE	SILVER	GOLD
Place value			
Ordering decimals			
A written method for addition			
A written method for subtraction			
A written method for multiplication			
A written method for division			
Using a calculator			
Checking your answers			
Fractions and percentages of quantities			
Factors, multiples and primes			
Coordinates in the first quadrant			
Reflective symmetry			
Drawing and measuring lines			
Perimeter			
Finding the area of rectangles			
Angles			
Frequency tables			
Multi-step problems			
Number patterns			
Solving problems			

■SCHOLASTIC
www.scholastic.co.uk

QUICK FIX FOR YEAR 6: MATHS

12-WEEK SATS REVISION PROGRAMME

Week 1	Week 2	Week 3
Introduce booster lessons and organise staff/equipment/	Mental warm-up	Mental warm-up
Revision timetable lesson	**Lessons 1 and 2:** Place value/ Ordering decimals	**Lessons 3 and 4:** Written methods for addition/ subtraction
Notes	Notes	Notes
Homework	Homework	Homework
Week 4	**Week 5**	**Week 6**
Mental warm-up	Mental warm-up	Mental warm-up
Lessons 5 and 6: Written methods for multiplication/ division	**Lessons 7 and 8:** Using a calculator/Checking your answers	**Lessons 9 and 10:** Fractions and percentages of quantities/ Factors, multiples and primes
Notes	Notes	Notes
Homework	Homework	Homework

Week 7	Week 8	Week 9
Mental warm-up	Mental warm-up	Mental warm-up
Lessons 11 and 12: Coordinates/Reflective symmetry	**Lessons 13 and 14:** Drawing and measuring lines/Perimeter	**Lessons 15 and 16:** Area of a rectangle/Angles
Notes	Notes	Notes
Homework	Homework	Homework
Week 10	**Week 11**	**Week 12**
Mental warm-up	Mental warm-up	Mental warm-up
Lessons 17 and 18: Frequency tables/Multi-step problems	**Lessons 19 and 20:** Number patterns/Solving puzzles	Sample tests
Notes	Notes	Notes
Homework	Homework	Homework

Name _____

1. Write in the missing numbers.   *2 marks*

$(5 \times 5) +$ [   ] $= 29$

$(4 \times 6) -$ [   ] $= 21$

2. Circle the three numbers which can be divided exactly by 5.   *1 mark*

15	21	35
33	64	40
37	6	99

3. Circle two numbers that add up to 80.   *1 mark*

26	21	35
42	59	10
57	66	32

4. Joshua has 23 football stickers. He puts them into groups
of five and gives them away to his friends.   *2 marks*

a) How many friends receive stickers? [   ]

b) How many stickers does Joshua have left? [   ]

5. Draw one line to join two fractions which have the same value. *1 mark*

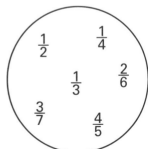

TOTAL

6. These thermometers show the temperatures in Liverpool
and Manchester.

3 marks

Liverpool

Manchester

What is the temperature in Liverpool? [　　　　]

What is the temperature in Manchester? [　　　　]

Write the missing number in this sentence: Liverpool is [　　　　]
degrees warmer than Manchester.

7. This chart shows how many points Amina scored on a
computer game.

3 marks

Round 1	86
Round 2	104
Round 3	61
Round 4	75
Round 5	93
Round 6	57

a) Write the scores in order starting with the smallest.

[　　　　　　　　　　　　　　　　　　　]

b) Find the difference between the largest and smallest number.

[　　　　]

c) In Round 7, Amina scored 26 more points than she did in Round 1.
How many points did she score in Round 7?

[　　　　]

TOTAL

[　]

Name _____

8. This pictogram shows the number of penny chews some children bought.

2 marks

 = 10 chews   = 5 chews

	Number of penny chews	Number of chews
Finley		
Jamie		
Stephanie		
Scarlett		
Leo		25

a) Write the number of chews each child bought in the last column.

b) Complete the pictogram by drawing the number of chews Leo bought.

TOTAL

9. *3 marks*

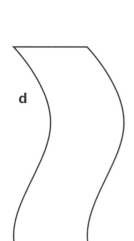

a) Which shapes have two lines of symmetry? ☐

b) Which shapes have one line of symmetry? ☐

c) Which shapes have no lines of symmetry? ☐

TOTAL

Name _____

10. Shade in 2 small squares on this grid.   *2 marks*

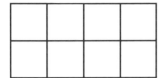

    a) What fraction of the grid have you shaded in?

    b) Write another way of showing this fraction.

11. If 8 x 40 = 320 what is 320 divided by 40?   *1 mark*

12.

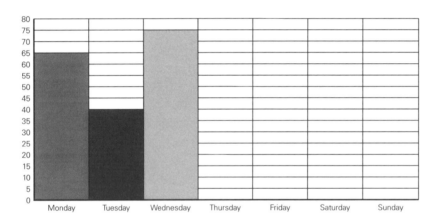

This table shows the number of minutes Hussein spent watching TV in a week.

Monday	65
Tuesday	40
Wednesday	75
Thursday	50
Friday	5
Saturday	80
Sunday	25

Complete the bar chart showing the number of minutes Hussein watched TV on Thursday, Friday, Saturday and Sunday.   *4 marks*

TOTAL

13. Draw a line from each name to the correct shape.   *3 marks*

Sphere

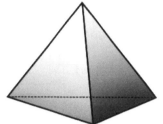

Cone

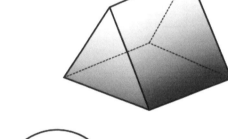

Cuboid

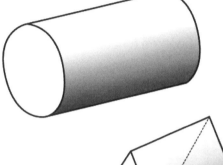

Cylinder

Triangular-based pyramid

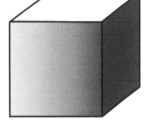

Triangular prism

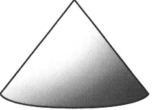

TOTAL

SCHOLASTIC
www.scholastic.co.uk

QUICK FIX FOR YEAR 6: MATHS

Name _____

14. For each of these amounts of money, write the number of pounds and number of pence.   *4 marks*

☐

a) £8.65 [   ] pounds [   ] pence

b) £10.54 [   ] pounds [   ] pence

c) £109.31 [   ] pounds [   ] pence

d) £287.90 [   ] pounds [   ] pence

15. Isabella and George have been on a nature trail.

a) Weight: For each of these objects tick to show whether they would be measured in grams or kilograms.   *1 mark*

☐

Large rock ☐ g ☐ kg   Tree trunk ☐ g ☐ kg

Pine cone ☐ g ☐ kg   Worm ☐ g ☐ kg

TOTAL

☐

b) Length: For each of these objects tick to show whether they would be measured in centimetres or metres.   *1 mark*

Spider ☐ cm ☐ m   Height of a tree ☐ cm ☐ m

Leaf ☐ cm ☐ m   Bridge ☐ cm ☐ m

c) Capacity: For each of these items tick to show whether their capacity should be measured in millilitres or litres.   *1 mark*

Pond ☐ ml ☐ l   Jam jar ☐ ml ☐ l

Teaspoon ☐ ml ☐ l   Bucket ☐ ml ☐ l

☐

TOTAL

☐

Total marks for the test = 35

QUICK FIX FOR YEAR 6: MATHS

Name _____

1. Write what the missing digits could be.   *2 marks*

    a) ☐☐☐ ÷ 10 = 5☐

    b) 8☐ x 10 = ☐0 0

2. Write what the missing numbers could be.   *2 marks*

    a) ☐ ÷ ☐ = 9

    b) ☐ x ☐ = 51

3. What are the missing numbers?   *2 marks*

    a) 457 + ☐ = 594

    b) 837 − 389 = ☐

4. Write these fractions in the correct boxes.   *2 marks*

$\frac{1}{10}$ $\frac{1}{2}$ $\frac{4}{7}$ $\frac{3}{4}$ $\frac{2}{3}$ $\frac{9}{18}$ $\frac{5}{12}$ $\frac{2}{5}$ $\frac{2}{9}$ $\frac{3}{6}$

Less than half	A half	More than half

TOTAL

SCHOLASTIC
www.scholastic.co.uk

5. Write these percentages in the correct boxes.   *2 marks*

25%, 33%, 61%, 50%, 74%, 48%, 7%

Less than half	A half	More than half

6. Write these decimals in the correct boxes.   *2 marks*

0.6, 0.33, 0.5, 1.65, 0.25, 1.5, 0.05

Less than half	A half	More than half

7. Charlie spends three hours a day travelling to work and home again on the train. What fraction of the day does Charlie spend on the train?   *1 mark*

8. Wesley jumped 1.21m in the high jump. Joseph jumped 35cm less. How high in metres did Joseph jump?   *1 mark*

TOTAL

Name _____

9. Andy needs a new tennis racket. He sees one in the sports shop priced £60. Then he sees the same racket in the department store for £90 but with a 50% discount. Which one should he buy? What is the difference in price?   *1 mark*

10. A tour of a football stadium starts at 11.27am and lasts for 45 minutes. At what time does it end?   *1 mark*

11. Here are the results of Tortoise Road Primary School's 100m race. Write in the table the names of the children in the order they finished – first at the top.   *2 marks*

Name	Time in seconds
Zac	19.6
Debbie	15.9
Lihan	22.1
Raj	19.4
Charlotte	16.7
Ricky	15.5
Meg	20.2
Jordan	16.9

Finishing order	Name
1st	
2nd	
3rd	
4th	
5th	
6th	
7th	
8th	

TOTAL

■SCHOLASTIC
www.scholastic.co.uk

12.

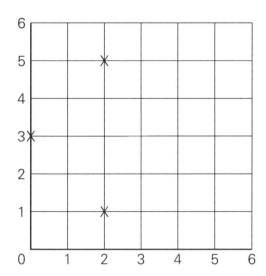

a) Place a cross at a position so that all four crosses complete the four vertices of a square. *1 mark*

b) What are the coordinates of the cross you have added? *1 mark*

TOTAL

13. a) Link the nets to the 3-D shapes. Draw a line to match them up.

4 marks

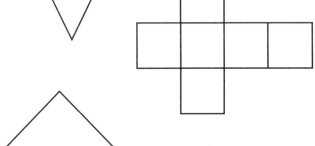

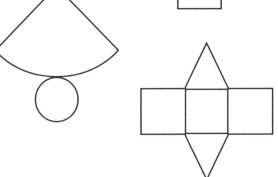

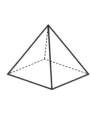

b) Circle the three nets which would form a cube.

2 marks

TOTAL

14. Study the 2-D shapes drawn on the grid.

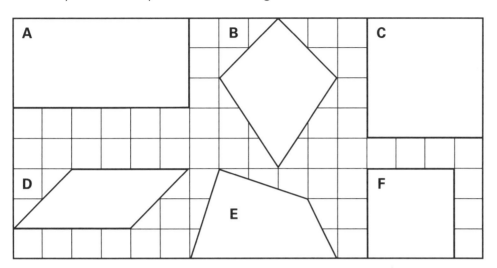

Fill in the table which sorts the shapes into three groups.
Put a tick in the box if the description fits.   *2 marks*

Shape	All angles are right angles	All sides equal in length	Opposite sides are parallel
A			
B			
C			
D			
E			
F			

15. The ages of Ally and Sally add up to 77. Ally's age is Sally's
reversed. How old are Ally and Sally?   *1 mark*

TOTAL

16. How many cubes are needed to turn this into a cuboid?   *1 mark*

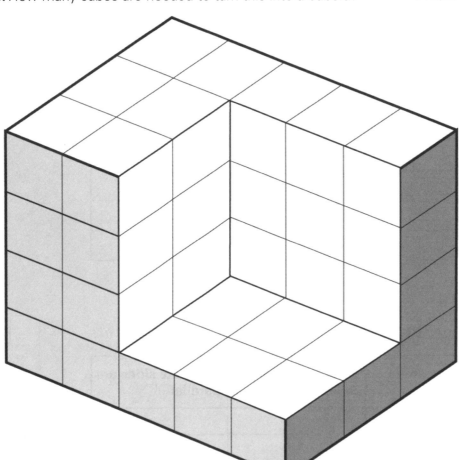

17. Two cartons of orange juice cost 72p. What is the cost of
5 cartons of orange juice at the same price per carton?
Show your method.   *2 marks*

18. Katie and Chantelle try to guess how many sweets there
are in a jar. Katie says 285 and Chantelle says 230. There
are 256 sweets in the jar. Who was closest to the correct
amount and by how many?   *2 marks*

TOTAL

19. Pravin and Courtney went to the fair. They each had £10 to spend.

a) If Pravin had a turn on each of the attractions would he have change from £10? If so, how much?

1 mark

b) Courtney had two rides on the Dodgems and two rides on the Big Wheel. He spent the rest of his money on two other attractions. What were they?

1 mark

TOTAL

Total marks for the test = 36

END OF YEAR OBJECTIVE
Y5: Explain what each digit represents in whole numbers

WHAT YOU NEED
■ Photocopiable page 35 for each pupil
■ Writing equipment

PLACE VALUE

INTRODUCTION

■ All numbers are made of digits.

■ These are all the digits: 0, 1, 2, 3, 4, 5, 6, 7, 8, 9.

■ The digits only have a value when they are given a place.

■ Where the digit is 'placed' in relation to the decimal point determines its value.

WHOLE CLASS TEACHING

■ Draw a large decimal point on the board. To the left of it write H T U.

■ Ask the group what they think H T U stands for. Hopefully you will get the correct response!

■ Now write a three-digit number under H T U and explain the value of each digit. For example, in 638, the 6 digit is worth 600 (6 x 100), the 3 digit is worth 30 (3 x 10) and the 8 digit is worth 8 (8 x 1).

■ Repeat the exercise with a different three-digit number chosen by a pupil.

■ Write 'Th' next to 'H'. Ask the group what they think 'Th' stands for.

■ Now write a four-digit number under Th H T U and explain the value of each digit.

■ Repeat with a different four-digit number chosen by a pupil. When you feel the group is ready, let them begin photocopiable page 35.

REVIEW

■ Go over the work completed by selecting pupils who may need the concepts reinforced to correctly run through a question.

■ Run through the questions with the group, correcting as you go.

■ Explain that the next lesson will deal with digits placed to the right of the decimal point.

■ The decimal point never 'moves'. It is always the digits that do the jumping around from place to place!

MAIN POINTS

■ Imagine each digit being in its own box. Each box is worth 10 times as much as the box to its right.
■ The further LEFT of the decimal point, the LARGER the value of the digit.
■ The decimal point separates whole numbers from fractions. Any digits to the right of the decimal point are less than one. (See next lesson.)

HOMEWORK

■ Make up five numbers of at least three digits, each using just the odd digits.
■ Write each of the five numbers in words (e.g. *638 is six hundred and thirty-eight*).

Place value

Hattie has five digit cards. They are 8, 6, 2, 5 and 3. For each question she can only use each card once. Write your answers in figures.

1. What is the largest three-digit number she can make?

2. What is the smallest three-digit number she can make?

3. What is the second largest three-digit number she can make?

4. What is the second smallest number she can make?

Hattie swaps her five digit cards for the remaining five. Again she can only use each card once in each answer. This time, write your answers in words and figures.

5. What is the largest four-digit number she can make?

6. What is the smallest four-digit number she can make?

7. What is the third largest four-digit number she can make?

8. What is the fourth smallest number she can make?

9. Place the digits 0, 1, 3, 5, 7 and 9 in the boxes to get the largest result. You can only use each digit once.

☐☐ x ☐☐ + ☐☐ = ☐☐☐☐

ORDERING DECIMALS

INTRODUCTION

■ Recap on the work done in Lesson 1 on place value. Write a three-digit number on the board and ask the pupils to identify the value of each digit.

■ Hand out the rulers and photocopiable page 37 to each pupil.

WHOLE CLASS TEACHING

■ Explain to the class that decimal numbers are not whole numbers. The decimal 4.8 is 'in between' 4 and 5. The decimal 3.6 is 'in between' 3 and 4.

■ Ask the class to find 4.8 (cm) on their rulers.

■ Explain that the rulers make perfect 'decimal number lines' if you view the centimetres as whole numbers from 1 to 30 and the millimetres as the tenths in between.

■ Write a decimal number on the board (63.82). Ask the class to give the value of each digit. (60, 3, then 8 tenths and 2 hundredths.)

■ Tell the class that in their tests they will have to answer questions in which they are asked to order decimal numbers by size. Set the class to work on photocopiable page 37.

REVIEW

■ Pick the 'Go for Gold!' question on the worksheet. Explain that this is a Level 5 question and that if they can answer this, then they are doing very well! Complete the question on the board with class.

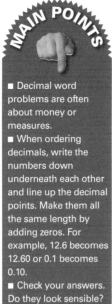

Ordering decimals

| Mehmet: 3.2m |
| Stanley: 4.1m |
| Grace: 3.6m |
| Harry: 3.8m |
| Rochelle: 2.1m |
| Billy: 1.7m |
| Mary: 2.5m |

This is a list of the distances jumped in the long jump competition at the school sports day by class 6A.

Write down the distances in order of size, starting with the longest jump.

Name	Distance
1st	
2nd	
3rd	
4th	
5th	
6th	

| Mehmet: 13.52m |
| Grace: 20.31m |
| Harry: 15.5m |
| Billy: 19.47m |
| Melissa: 13.75m |
| Isabella: 18.2m |
| Mary: 13.25m |

Class 6A then took part in a javelin competition. These are the results.

Write down the distances in order of size, starting with the furthest throw.

Name	Distance
1st	
2nd	
3rd	
4th	
5th	
6th	

These are the times of six athletes who competed in a 100m final. They were timed to a thousandth of a second. Sort the times so you find the finishing order and complete the table below.

| Christie: 10.003s |
| Lewis: 10.318s |
| Thompson: 10.061s |
| Wells: 9.995s |
| Crawford: 9.909s |
| Greene: 10.381s |

Name	Time
1st	
2nd	
3rd	
4th	
5th	
6th	

END OF YEAR OBJECTIVE
Y5: Use efficient written methods to add and subtract whole numbers and decimals with up to two places

WHAT YOU NEED
■ Photocopiable page 39 for each pupil
■ Writing equipment

A WRITTEN METHOD FOR ADDITION

INTRODUCTION

■ Explain to the class that they have three choices when faced with an addition sum. They should first try the calculation mentally. If it is too hard then they need to use a reliable written method. If it is still too hard then they should use a calculator.

■ They will only be allowed to use a calculator on one of their test papers so they need to have a reliable method for addition using a paper and pencil.

WHOLE CLASS TEACHING

■ Write H T U on the board. Ask for two three-digit numbers. Line them up under the H T U. Ask for an estimate of the total of the two numbers. Perform the calculation using the column method. Start with the units, then the tens and then the hundreds. If the two numbers chosen don't require you to 'carry' then repeat the demonstration with two numbers that do. Check the calculation. Was the estimate close?

■ Tell the class that before attempting any calculation they should approach it by following this method; **Estimate, Calculate, Check**. Reinforce this throughout the lesson.

■ Set the class to work on photocopiable page 39.

REVIEW

■ Go over any questions which may have caused problems.

■ Set the group a challenge! Ask for each of them to give a two-, three- or four- digit number. Write them on the board in column form (correctly aligned). Aim for at least ten numbers to add. Ask for estimates of the answer and jot them down next to the calculation. You could put the initials of each pupil next to their estimate. Work through the calculation as a group. Talk about what you are doing at each stage. Check your answer. Whose estimate was closest? This should be a fun and confidence boosting end to the lesson!

■ Practise this method of addition until it is second nature. It is a vital skill which will stay with you for life!

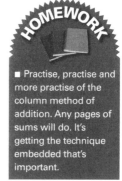

MAIN POINTS

■ Think about the value of the digits they have to carry. Is the 1 digit worth one, ten or a hundred?
■ Remember: **Estimate, Calculate, Check!**
■ Remember to line up the calculation properly. You can refer back to the previous lessons about place value.

HOMEWORK

■ Practise, practise and more practise of the column method of addition. Any pages of sums will do. It's getting the technique embedded that's important.

A written method for addition

Put these numbers into columns and add them using the column method.

1. How many are 63 and 78 altogether?

3. Find the sum of these numbers: 23, 34, 45, 56.

2. What is the total of 85, 76 and 92?

4. Add 59, 69, 79, 89 and 99.

Add these numbers using the column method.

5. 384, 593, 882

8. 470, 529, 448

6. 504, 669, 274

9. 269, 692, 487

7. 729, 834, 929

Now try these. Be careful when adding the decimals; remember the decimal point.

10. 4825 + 7923

13. 23.5 + 62.7

11. 4926 + 3517 + 6352

14. 49.84 + 72.39

12. 6935 + 6924 + 2251

15. 94.27 + 73.77

SCHOLASTIC
www.scholastic.co.uk

QUICK FIX FOR YEAR 6: MATHS

A WRITTEN METHOD FOR SUBTRACTION

INTRODUCTION

■ Ask the class what they must do before tackling a calculation and afterwards. Reinforce the **Estimate, Calculate, Check** way of thinking.

■ Again, remind them that they need an efficient and reliable method of subtraction using a paper and pencil.

WHOLE CLASS TEACHING

■ Same procedure as in the previous lesson. Write H T U on the board and request two three-digit numbers. Place the largest number at the top. Ask the class for their estimates and perform the subtraction using the column method. If there is no need to 'carry' then repeat the demonstration with two numbers that do require carrying. Check your answer. How close were the estimates?

■ Set the class to work on photocopiable page 41.

REVIEW

■ Go over any questions which have caused problems.

■ At this point, try to establish whether everyone in the group is confident using the two methods of calculation taught so far. Inform them that if they can add or subtract a three-digit number with another three-digit number, they are doing well. If they can add and subtract four-digit numbers, they are doing brilliantly! (Once the technique has been grasped there's no real reason why they shouldn't be able to do the calculations with any number of digits. You could demonstrate this with a more able pupil in your group – or yourself.)

DON'T PANIC!

■ Make sure the children are familiar with the language of subtraction: 'find the difference between', 'subtract', 'how many less than', and so on.

MAIN POINTS

■ Reinforce the **Estimate, Calculate, Check** rule. Do their answers look sensible?
■ Depending on your group, you could tell the group that you know this isn't the most exciting task they've ever done. You just want to equip them with the tools to succeed. These written methods of calculation should become second nature and will remain with them for life.
■ Again, think about the value of the digits they are 'borrowing' and 'carrying'. Are they thousands, hundreds, tens or units?

HOMEWORK

■ 'Practise and then more practise. When you've finished practising, then practise some more!' Use old books of sums or make your own up. Keep at it until the method for subtraction is firmly fixed in your mind.

A written method for subtraction

Estimate an answer before doing these calculations using the column method. Use the back of this sheet for your working out.

1. What is the difference between 31 and 75?

3. Take away 48 from 83.

2. Subtract 57 from 92.

4. What is 67 minus 25?

Now try these.

5. 683 – 592

8. 702 – 295

6. 993 – 478

9. 427 – 218

7. 563 – 247

Remember the decimal point when subtracting decimals. Check your answers. Do they look sensible?

10. 6283 – 776

13. 5.35 – 2.73

11. 2296 – 1837

14. 18.28 – 13.33

12. 9282 – 3006

15. 94.72 – 73.56

A WRITTEN METHOD FOR MULTIPLICATION

INTRODUCTION

■ Ask the class what the routine is when tackling a calculation. (**Estimate**, **Calculate**, **Check**)

■ Remind the class that they need to learn a reliable written method of multiplication.

WHOLE CLASS TEACHING

■ Ask for two two-digit numbers which you are going to multiply. Ask the class for estimates for the answer. Multiply them together using the column method explaining the process as you go. Check the answer and review the estimates – which was closest?

■ Repeat the exercise until everyone feels confident using the column method.

■ Periodically stop the group and ask them to think about the value of the digits they are multiplying.

■ Ask if anyone has got a good method for estimating. Show the class the rounding method (covered in a later lesson). Write 32 x 87 on the board. Round to 30 x 90 and with your knowledge of tables you can estimate an answer of 2700. Calculate using the column method to give an answer of 2784. Your answer is very close to your estimate!

■ Explain that instant recall of the tables makes multiplying any numbers very easy. You could demonstrate this by asking for a six-digit number and multiplying it by a single-digit number, explaining that you never need to go beyond the range of 9 x 9. Anyone who needs to practise their tables should make it their top priority when revising at home.

■ Set the class to work on photocopiable page 43.

REVIEW

■ Go over any questions which have caused difficulty.

■ Try to ensure that everyone is happy with the column method for multiplication. Anyone who is still unsure, needs to practise more!

A written method for multiplication

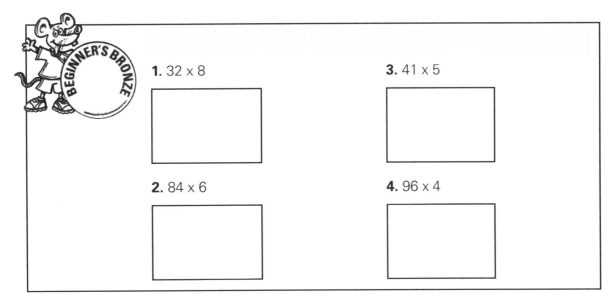

BEGINNER'S BRONZE

1. 32 x 8

3. 41 x 5

2. 84 x 6

4. 96 x 4

STEADY SILVER

Now try these.

5. 527 x 3

8. 84 x 67

6. 836 x 5

9. 59 x 38

7. 73 x 35

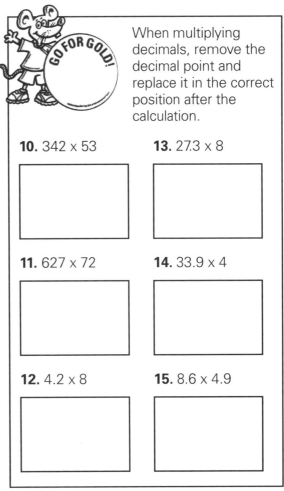

GO FOR GOLD!

When multiplying decimals, remove the decimal point and replace it in the correct position after the calculation.

10. 342 x 53

13. 27.3 x 8

11. 627 x 72

14. 33.9 x 4

12. 4.2 x 8

15. 8.6 x 4.9

SCHOLASTIC
www.scholastic.co.uk

A WRITTEN METHOD FOR DIVISION

INTRODUCTION

■ Ask the class whether anyone has difficulty with division. You may get quite a few affirmative replies. Explain that they are going to learn and practise a written method which they will be able to rely on and use with confidence.

■ Explain that once the technique has been learnt they can have a go at long division which is into the realms of Level 5 and beyond!

WHOLE CLASS TEACHING

■ Ask the class for a three-digit number and a single-digit number. Write them on the board as a division sum. Ask for an estimate of the answer before performing the calculation.

■ Talk through each step of the operation until you get to the answer.

■ Repeat the exercise and ask the class to identify each step that you make. You should be able to come up with this 'formula' for dividing a three-digit number by a single-digit number:

■ Divide into the three-digit number, one digit at a time, starting from the left.

■ Put the answer of each division on the top.

■ If the one-digit number doesn't divide exactly into the digit in the three-digit number then carry the remainder to the next digit on the right.

■ If it doesn't go at all, put a 0 on top (the answer line) and carry the whole digit.

■ Work another example on the board: 636 ÷ 6.

■ Set the class to work on photocopiable page 45.

REVIEW

■ If the class is progressing well, try introducing 'long division' by doing an example of a three- or four-digit number divided by a two-digit number. Show the example clearly on the board.

■ The 'long division' work is Level 5 material. Master the HTU ÷ U to be a secure Level 4 in division.

MAIN POINTS

■ Knowing your tables is vital for division as well as multiplication.
■ Remember to check your answers by using the inverse of division – multiplication.
■ Be systematic and methodical in your working – especially when doing long division calculations.

HOMEWORK

■ The goal is for everyone to have mastered the written methods for all four operations. Practise all four until they become second nature.

A written method for division

Use the back of this sheet for your working out.

1. 35 ÷ 5

4. 54 ÷ 3

2. 66 ÷ 9

5. 88 ÷ 4

3. 71 ÷ 4

6. 100 ÷ 5

Use the back of this sheet for your working out.

7. 140 ÷ 7

10. 564 ÷ 6

8. 156 ÷ 6

11. 704 ÷ 9

9. 348 ÷ 3

12. 786 ÷ 8

Use the back of this sheet for your working out.

13. 216 ÷ 12

16. 528 ÷ 16

14. 345 ÷ 15

17. 1232 ÷ 22

15. 703 ÷ 19

18. 2475 ÷ 25

USING A CALCULATOR

INTRODUCTION

■ Explain that using a calculator is not the answer to all mathematical problems. In fact, unless they are used properly they can be a hindrance because too much faith is placed in their answers.

■ The SATs will test your ability to use a calculator correctly.

■ Calculators should be used when the calculation is too difficult to do in your head or with a written method. Don't forget, you should always make an estimate of an answer before using the calculator.

WHOLE CLASS TEACHING

■ Hand out photocopiable page 47 and a calculator to each pupil. Study the diagram of the calculator on the sheet. Identify the function of each key on the calculator.

■ Teach these five steps to calculator success. The pupils can note these down for future reference.

■ Step 1: Read the question. Does it need a calculator?

■ Step 2: Press the keys carefully and methodically.

■ Step 3: Check the display to see if you've pressed the correct buttons.

■ Step 4: Press the 'equals' key after each calculation.

■ Step 5: Check your answer. Does it look correct? If not, take a few seconds to re-do the calculation.

■ Set the class to work through the questions on photocopiable page 47 using the calculator.

REVIEW

■ Reinforce the five steps to calculator success. These could be turned into a poster and displayed on the wall or written on A5 and stuck in to their books and folders.

Using a calculator

Try these simple calculations to get you started.

1. 637 + 397 = [   ]

2. 832 – 466 = [   ]

3. 77 x 44 = [   ]

4. 5220 ÷ 36 = [   ]

Now try these.

5. 963 ÷ 12 = [   ]

6. 424 x 42.4 = [   ]

7. 909 ÷ 0.09 = [   ]

8. 73.8 – 4.9 = [   ]

percentage   display

square root   all clear

memory   clear

buttons

ten digits

decimal point

equals   plus/minus

four operations

9. – 4 + 6 = [   ]

10. (– 42 + 54) – 21 = [   ]

11. (3.3 + 5.75) x 7.9= [   ]

12. (124 x 5) – 339 = [   ]

13. £862.74 – [   ] = £275.95

LESSON PLANS

END OF YEAR OBJECTIVES

Y5: Use knowledge of rounding, place value, number facts and inverse operations to estimate and check calculations.

Y6: Use approximations, inverse operations and tests of divisibility to estimate and check results.

WHAT YOU NEED

■ Writing equipment
■ Photocopiable page 49 for each pupil

CHECKING YOUR ANSWERS

INTRODUCTION

■ Explain that you are going to teach two methods of checking your answers to a calculation – the 'inverse method' and the 'rounding method'.

■ Lots of marks can be saved in tests by pupils checking their answers and correcting mistakes.

WHOLE CLASS TEACHING

■ Refer back to 'A Written Method for Multiplication' and revise the rounding method for estimating an answer. It is just as useful when checking your answers. If your answer is close to your estimate from rounding then it is probably correct. If you are still not sure then check using the inverse method.

■ Inverse means 'opposite'. The inverse of addition is subtraction. The inverse of multiplication is division. You do the opposite operation to your answer to check that it gives you back the number you started with.

   ■ Example 1: What is the difference between 526 and 362?

   ■ Calculate: 526 – 362 = 164

   ■ Check: 164 + 362 = 526

   ■ Example 2: What is 13 multiplied by 17?

   ■ Calculate: 13 x 17 = 221

   ■ Check: 221 ÷ 17 = 13

■ Set the class to work on photocopiable page 49.

REVIEW

■ Establish that everyone in the group can check an answer using one or both of the methods – even on simple calculations.

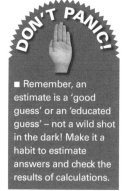

■ Remember, an estimate is a 'good guess' or an 'educated guess' – not a wild shot in the dark! Make it a habit to estimate answers and check the results of calculations.

MAIN POINTS

■ Get into the habit of always checking your answers; it will gain you marks in the tests.
■ Does your answer 'look right'? Think about the question – does your answer make sense?
■ When adding several numbers, try adding them again but backwards. The answer should be the same; it doesn't matter what order you add numbers together.

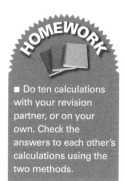

HOMEWORK

■ Do ten calculations with your revision partner, or on your own. Check the answers to each other's calculations using the two methods.

Checking your answers

Use the inverse method to check your answers to these calculations. Use another sheet of paper to show your working.

1. 424 − 67 = [ ]   Check: [ ] + 67 = [ ]

2. 168 ÷ 4 = [ ]   Check: [ ] x 4 = [ ]

3. 396 + 42 = [ ]   Check: [ ] − 42 = [ ]

4. 75 x 3 = [ ]   Check: [ ] ÷ 3 = [ ]

Use the rounding method to check your answers to these calculations. Use another sheet of paper to show your working.

5. 787 x 11 = [ ]   Rough answer [ ]

6. 381 − 112 = [ ]   Rough answer [ ]

7. 504 ÷ 18 = [ ]   Rough answer [ ]

8. 482 + 391 = [ ]   Rough answer [ ]

These are eight answers to a maths test. Mark the answers and write the score below.
Check the answers carefully using both methods. Use another sheet of paper to show your working.

9. 612 + 485 + 309 = 1406

10. 1387 − 594 − 118 = 575

11. 688 x 18 = 12 384

12. 945 ÷ 15 = 63

13. 1973 + 4612 + 8892 = 15 577

14. 2967 − 32 − 688 = 2247

15. 998 x 112 = 111 775

16. 684 ÷ 19 = 36

Total: [ ] /8

SCHOLASTIC
www.scholastic.co.uk

QUICK FIX FOR YEAR 6: MATHS

FRACTIONS AND PERCENTAGES OF QUANTITIES

INTRODUCTION

■ Explain that these questions can appear in different ways in the SATs. They might be asked in 'word problem' style so the question takes on a real-life feel. Other ways include looking at shapes that have been shaded, and finding fractions and percentages of measures and money.

WHOLE CLASS LEARNING

■ Write the following problem on the board: School children have a total of 13 weeks' holiday per year. What fraction of the year do they spend at school?

■ Ask the class to spend a couple of minutes working out the answer. Work through the problem with the class, discussing points as they arise. Did anyone answer $\frac{1}{4}$? Encourage the class to read the problem carefully.

■ Emphasise the point of reading the question and then reading it again to make sure they understand what they are being asked to do. Again, many marks can be saved in tests by not rushing and by working systematically.

■ At some point in the lesson stop the class and remind them that they should know as many fraction, decimal and percentage equivalents as possible. Write up the equivalents for 1 whole, $\frac{1}{2}$, $\frac{1}{4}$, $\frac{3}{4}$, $\frac{1}{3}$, $\frac{1}{5}$, $\frac{1}{10}$ on the board. Children who don't know them all should write them in their books or make a note and make sure they learn them.

■ Set the class to work on photocopiable page 51.

REVIEW

■ Ask the class which type of questions they found the hardest and easiest. Go over the questions which caused the most problems (if any).

■ Tell the class that they will probably have at least one of these types of questions in the mental maths test.

Fractions and percentages of quantities

Write down the answers to the following calculations.

1. $\frac{1}{5}$ of £3 = ☐

2. $\frac{3}{4}$ of £8 = ☐

3. $\frac{1}{10}$ of £15 = ☐

4. $\frac{1}{3}$ of £18 = ☐

5. 25% of 200kg = ☐

6. 50% of 9 litres = ☐

7. 20% of 1km = ☐

8. 75% of an hour = ☐ minutes

What fraction of each of these rectangles is shaded?

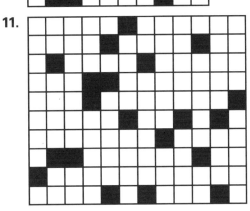

9.

10.

11.

Liam asked 40 children in his year to name their favourite pop group. Here are the results of his survey.

Group	Number of children
The Kaiser Chefs	8
No Girls Allowed	10
Take That and Go!	4
The Sugar-lumps	18

12. Which group did 20% of the children say was their favourite? Show your working on another sheet of paper.

☐

END OF YEAR OBJECTIVES
Y5: Identify pairs of factors of two-digit whole numbers and find common multiples
Y6: Recognise that prime numbers have only two factors and identify prime numbers less than 100; find the prime factors of two-digit numbers

WHAT YOU NEED
■ Writing equipment
■ Photocopiable page 53 for each pupil

FACTORS, MULTIPLES AND PRIMES

INTRODUCTION

■ Ask the class what they know about factors, multiples and prime numbers.

■ Explain that this lesson is going to be about clarifying these terms so that everybody is confident about answering questions about them in the SATs.

■ Tell the class that you are going to let them know how they could win $100,000 at the end of the lesson! (As long as they get their work done.)

WHOLE CLASS TEACHING

■ Write the words 'Factors', Multiples' and 'Prime numbers' as headings on the board.

■ Explain that we need definitions for each one.

■ Get the class to come up with these definitions!

　■ **Factors** are numbers that divide exactly into other numbers.

　■ **Multiples** are numbers made by multiplying two numbers together.

　■ **Prime numbers** are numbers that can only be divided by themselves and ONE.

■ Once everyone is clear about the definitions, set the class to work on photocopiable page 53.

REVIEW

■ Ensure everyone is clear about the definitions.

■ Now tell them about the Mersenne Project (www.mersenne.org) which offers a cash prize of $100,000 to the person or group which discovers the first 10-million-digit prime number using their home computer. Read up about the project on the website.

MAIN POINTS

■ New prime numbers are still being found. The largest known prime number is nearly 10 million digits long!
■ 1 is not a prime number.
■ Everyone should study the tips on multiples in the Go for Gold! section.

DON'T PANIC!

■ Explore prime numbers over 100. Which is the largest prime number the children can find? How can they test whether a number is prime?

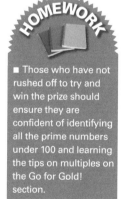

HOMEWORK

■ Those who have not rushed off to try and win the prize should ensure they are confident of identifying all the prime numbers under 100 and learning the tips on multiples on the Go for Gold! section.

Factors, multiples and primes

The factors of the number 12 are: 1, 2, 3, 4, 6 and 12. What are the factors of the following numbers?

1. 16 _____

2. 20 _____

3. 32 _____

4. 100 _____

5. List all the prime numbers up to 100.

_____

_____

_____

Multiples tips – learn them!

■ If a number is a multiple of 2, the last digit will be even. (e.g. 204, 306, 508)

■ If a number is a multiple of 3, the sum of its digits can be divided by 3. (e.g. 117: 1 + 1 + 7 = 9; 11 835: 1 + 1 + 8 + 3 + 5 = 18)

■ If a number is a multiple of 4, its last two digits can be divided by 4. (e.g. 816: last two digits are 16)

■ If a number is a multiple of 5, the last digit is a 0 or 5. (e.g. 3935, 410)

■ If a number is a multiple of 6, it must be an even number and the sum of its digits must be divisible by 3. (e.g. 1482: 1 + 4 + 8 + 2 = 15)

■ If a number is a multiple of 7 – well, there are no tips for this one, you'll just have to divide by 7 and find out!

■ If a number is a multiple of 8, then half of the number is divisible by 4. (e.g. 520 ÷ 2 = 260: last two digits are 60; 60 ÷ 4 = 15)

■ If a number is a multiple of 9, then the sum of its digits is divisible by 9. (e.g. 387: 3 + 8 + 7 = 18)

■ If a number is a multiple of 10, then the last digit is 0. (e.g. 380, 1010)

COORDINATES IN THE FIRST QUADRANT

INTRODUCTION

■ Point to the map on the board and explain that coordinates are used to identify an exact point on a grid. They are very useful on maps and charts but can be used in a variety of ways.

■ We can use coordinates in four quadrants but we will be focusing on using them in the *first quadrant* only. Illustrate this by pointing to where the other three quadrants would be, in turn. (Quadrants work anti-clockwise: Quadrant 1 is 3 o'clock to 12 o'clock; quadrant 2 is 12 o'clock to 9 o'clock; quadrant 3 is 9 o'clock to 6 o'clock; quadrant 4 is 6 o'clock to 3 o'clock.)

WHOLE CLASS TEACHING

■ Ask the class to use coordinates to identify one of the positions on the map and write it on the board to model the recording of coordinates.

■ Ask the class what would happen if you recorded the digits within the brackets the wrong way round.

■ Set the class to work on photocopiable page 55.

REVIEW

■ Depending on the progress of your class, you could introduce them to using all four quadrants – this will be Level 5 material. If not, ensure the concepts covered in this lesson are firmly embedded as questions about coordinates will always appear in a SATs paper.

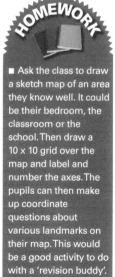

Coordinates in the first quadrant

Look at the map below.
1. What can be found at (4, 12)? _____

2. What are the coordinates for the Watch Tower? _____

3. Where might you see mermaids? _____

On the map below:
4. What are the four coordinates for the vertices of the fort?

_____

5. If you travelled from (5, 14) to (3, 2), where did you start from and where did you end up?

_____

6. Draw a line from (5, 14) to (9, 13) and another from (9, 13) to (8, 8). Now draw a line from (8, 8) back to (5, 14). What shape have you drawn?

_____

7. If Skull Rock and Dead Man's Tree form two vertices of a rectangle, give two other coordinates to form a rectangle.

_____

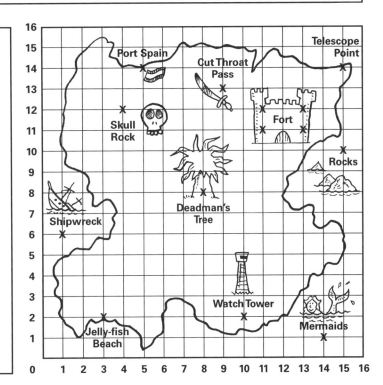

END OF YEAR OBJECTIVES
Y5: Complete patterns with up to two lines of symmetry; draw the position of a shape after a reflection
Y6: Visualise and draw on grids of different types where a shape will be after reflection

WHAT YOU NEED
■ Writing equipment
■ A mirror for each pupil (they will require one each for the SATs, so it would be good to organise it now!)
■ Coloured pencils
■ Photocopiable page 57 for each pupil

REFLECTIVE SYMMETRY

INTRODUCTION

■ Discuss the definition of 'reflective symmetry'. Ask the pupils for ideas of what they think it is.

■ Write on the board: 'A shape has reflective symmetry if both sides are the same when a mirror line is drawn.'

WHOLE CLASS TEACHING

■ Draw a capital 'W' and a capital 'H' on the board and ask the children to think about where the lines of symmetry are on each shape. Invite the children to explain their thoughts and reasoning.

■ Draw the one line of symmetry on the W and the two lines of symmetry on the H.

■ Stress the need for accuracy when drawing reflections. Explain to the class that they can check their drawings with a mirror, and encourage them to do so.

■ Set the class to work on photocopiable page 57.

■ Reflecting the shapes in the Bronze section is Level 3 standard, Silver is Level 4 and Gold is Level 5. Make this clear to the pupils. Ask them to spot the difference between the sets of questions. All the group need to be aiming at successfully completing the Silver section. To get to the required Level 4, they need to be able to reflect shapes where either the shape or the mirror line, or both, are at an angle.

■ Use the coloured pencils to colour the pattern in the Gold section in a symmetrical fashion. (Not required for SATs but will consolidate understanding of reflective symmetry)

REVIEW

■ Establish whether everyone can reach the Level 4 standard i.e. are happy with the Steady Silver section.

■ Compare completed patterns from the Go for Gold! section.

MAIN POINTS

■ Be careful when reflecting shapes that are at an angle to their mirror line.
■ Circles have an infinite number of lines of symmetry.
■ Don't be afraid to trust your eyes when looking at reflected shapes! Do they look right? If they look wrong, they probably are wrong.

DON'T PANIC!

■ When sketching a reflection, picture what the reflection will look like before you draw it. Using your imagination can be very useful in many areas of maths.

HOMEWORK

■ Using squared paper, practise drawing symmetrical patterns and reflecting shapes in mirror lines.

PHOTOCOPIABLE

Reflective symmetry

Draw the reflections of these shapes.

1.

2.

3.

4.

Draw the reflections of these shapes.

5.

6.

7.

Draw the reflections of these shapes.

8.

9.

10.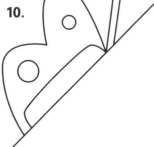

DRAWING AND MEASURING LINES

END OF YEAR OBJECTIVES
Y5: Draw and measure lines to the nearest millimetre

WHAT YOU NEED
■ Sharp pencils
■ 30cm rulers
■ Photocopiable page 59 for each pupil

INTRODUCTION

■ Stress the need for accuracy when drawing lines. Ask the class what factors might hinder their chances of completing what looks like a simple task – drawing a straight line! Having a blunt pencil is the main culprit.

■ Tell the class that in order to achieve a Level 4 they need to 'Draw and measure lines to the nearest millimetre'. This is very difficult to do with a blunt pencil.

WHOLE CLASS WORK

■ Ensure pencils are sharpened. (This could easily take up a couple of minutes of valuable lesson time; if possible, have the pencils sharpened before the lesson.)

■ Set the class to work on photocopiable page 59.

■ Early on in the session, stop the class to define *parallel* and *perpendicular* lines. Ensure everyone is clear on what they are. If need be, write the definitions in their books:

■ **Parallel lines:** equidistant; never meet, however far they are produced.

■ **Perpendicular:** a line or plane that is at right angles to another line or plane.

Allow the class to continue before stopping again to define *vertical* and *horizontal* lines. Again, ensure everyone is clear about what they are:

■ **Vertical line:** a line at right angles to the horizontal plane.

■ **Horizontal line:** parallel to the horizon.

REVIEW

■ Re-cap on the definitions of 'parallel', 'perpendicular', 'vertical' and 'horizontal'. These are terms the pupils need to know in order to achieve a Level 4.

■ If there is time, the pupils could swap their papers and check each other's measurements.

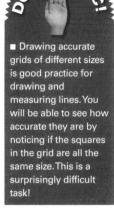

■ Drawing accurate grids of different sizes is good practice for drawing and measuring lines. You will be able to see how accurate they are by noticing if the squares in the grid are all the same size. This is a surprisingly difficult task!

■ As with calculations, it is always wise to double check any measurements you make. Work carefully and concentrate!
■ When measuring, be careful not to start measuring from the '1cm' mark on the ruler instead of the '0'.
■ Use decimal notation to record measurements (e.g. 4.6cm, 25.3cm and so on).

■ Practise measuring around the home. Challenge the pupils to find something which measures exactly 29.5cm (or any irregular length).
■ Practise drawing 2D shapes with parallel, perpendicular, vertical and horizontal lines.

Drawing and measuring lines

Measure these lines to the nearest millimetre.

1. _____

2. | 3. \   4. ╱

Starting from the dots, draw straight lines of the following lengths.

5. 8.5cm •

6. 11.3cm •

7. 15.7cm •

Connect the four dots to the single dot and write the lengths of your lines in millimetres on each line.

8. •   •

9. •

10. •

11. •

■SCHOLASTIC
www.scholastic.co.uk

QUICK FIX FOR YEAR 6: MATHS

PERIMETER

INTRODUCTION

■ Define the word 'perimeter': the **perimeter** of a shape is the distance all the way around its edge.

■ Tell the class that in order to achieve a Level 4 they need to 'Measure and calculate the perimeter of regular and irregular polygons'. Establish that everyone knows what regular and irregular polygons are:

■ **Regular polygon:** a 2-D shape where all angles and sides are of equal size.

■ **Irregular polygon:** a 2-D shape where at least one angle or length is a different size.

WHOLE CLASS LEARNING

■ Start work on photocopiable page 61.

■ Early in the session, ask the class if they can think of a way to remember the definition of the word 'perimeter'. If they struggle, mention the fact that a perimeter fence goes all the way around a building like a prison or football stadium – anything which will help them remember!

■ Stress the difference between 'measure' and 'calculate'. Some questions will require them to measure accurately to the nearest millimetre with a ruler. However, other shapes may have measurements written on them which are not to scale. With these types of questions, DON'T measure the sides with a ruler! Sometimes there will be missing lengths (as in the Go for Gold! questions); the reason they are missing is to test whether you can calculate them from the lengths you've been given.

REVIEW

■ Compare answers and discuss any problems.

■ Ensure everyone is clear on the definition of 'perimeter' and understands the difference between 'measuring' and 'calculating'.

Name _____

Perimeter

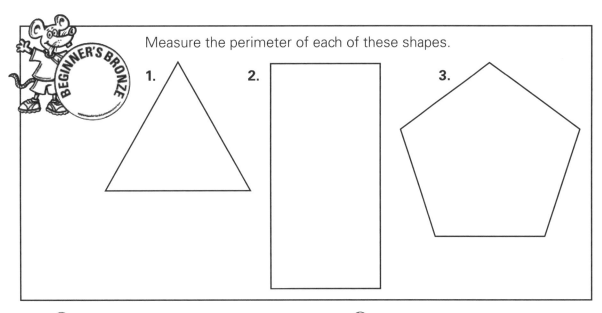

Measure the perimeter of each of these shapes.

1. **2.** **3.**

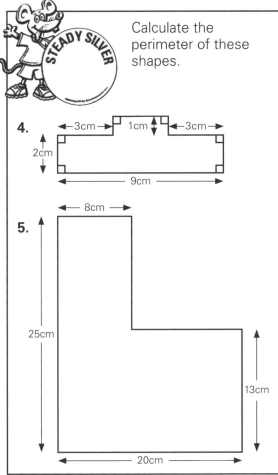

Calculate the perimeter of these shapes.

4. 3cm 1cm 3cm 2cm 9cm

5. 8cm 25cm 13cm 20cm

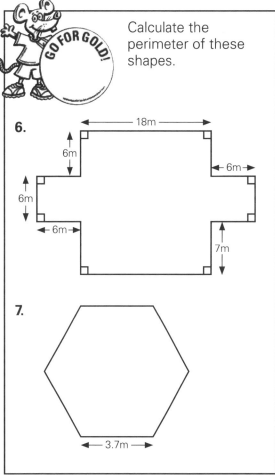

Calculate the perimeter of these shapes.

6. 18m 6m 6m 6m 6m 7m

7. 3.7m

■SCHOLASTIC
www.scholastic.co.uk

QUICK FIX FOR YEAR 6: **MATHS**

FINDING THE AREA OF RECTANGLES

INTRODUCTION

■ Discuss and establish the properties of a rectangle. In order to achieve a Level 4, the pupils need to know the following:

  ■ All four angles in a rectangle are right angles.

  ■ The opposite sides are parallel and equal.

  ■ The diagonals bisect each other.

  ■ Rectangles have two lines of symmetry.

WHOLE CLASS TEACHING

■ Discuss the term 'area': The area of a shape is the amount of surface it covers.

■ Explain that the formula for finding the area of a rectangle is length times breadth ($l \times b$). Ensure all pupils know this.

■ Demonstrate by drawing a large rectangle on the board. Label its sides 3cm and 2cm. (Explain that it is not to scale.)

■ Ask the class how to work out the area of the rectangle and perform the calculation as a group.

■ When the children have grasped the concept, set them to work on photocopiable page 63.

REVIEW

■ Re-cap on the formula for finding the area of a rectangle.

■ If the concept has been thoroughly grasped, introduce the following point: 'You can work out the area of a right-angled triangle by turning it into a rectangle, calculating its area and then halving the answer.' Demonstrate this on the board.

■ Ask the pupils if they can come up with a formula for this. (Area of a right-angled triangle $= \frac{1}{2}$ base x height)

■ Tell them that if they understand this, they are flying; this is heading towards Year 7 work.

DON'T PANIC!
■ Again, use your imagination when finding the area of shapes which can be divided into rectangles. Picture the rectangles within the shape before drawing them in.

MAIN POINTS
■ Make sure the units of area are always squared, for example cm² or m².
■ You can find the area of rectangles (and other shapes) drawn on centimetre grids by counting the number of squares it covers. Remember the answer will be in centimetres squared (cm²).

HOMEWORK
■ Draw a number of different rectangles on squared paper and calculate their areas. This would be a good activity to do with a 'revision buddy'.

Finding the area of rectangles

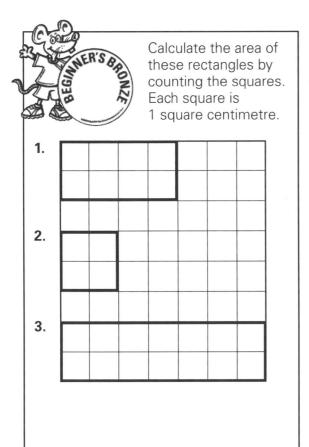

Calculate the area of these rectangles by counting the squares. Each square is 1 square centimetre.

1.

2.

3.

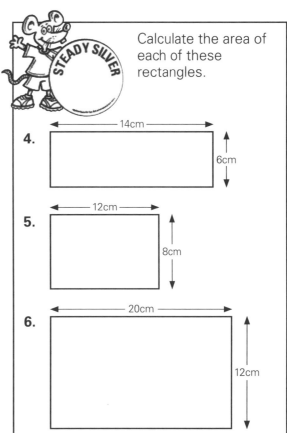

Calculate the area of each of these rectangles.

4. 14cm, 6cm

5. 12cm, 8cm

6. 20cm, 12cm

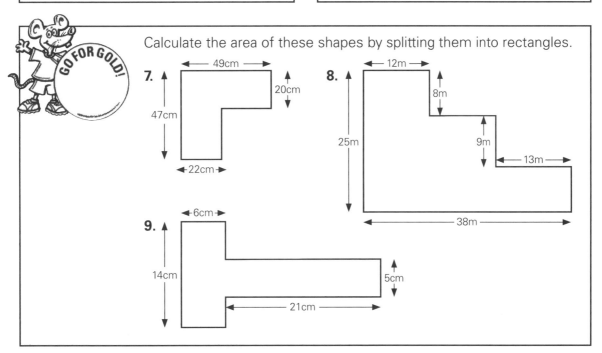

Calculate the area of these shapes by splitting them into rectangles.

7. 49cm, 20cm, 47cm, 22cm

8. 12m, 8m, 9m, 13m, 25m, 38m

9. 6cm, 14cm, 5cm, 21cm

QUICK FIX FOR YEAR 6: MATHS

ANGLES

INTRODUCTION

- Explain that there is a lot to cover in one lesson, so students must concentrate and have their eyes on the board.

WHOLE CLASS TEACHING

- In order to achieve a Level 4 the pupils need to know the following facts. Draw examples of each on the board and write these facts for the pupils to learn.

  - Angles are measured in degrees. (Show the little ° symbol.)

  - A whole turn is 360 degrees.

  - A right angle is a quarter turn and is 90 degrees.

  - A straight line is 180 degrees.

  - An acute angle is less than 90 degrees.

  - An obtuse angle is more than 90 but less than 180 degrees.

  - A reflex angle is more than 180 but less than 360 degrees.

  - The internal angles of a triangle add up to 180 degrees.

- Demonstrate the use of a protractor for those who have never used one – maybe quite a few.

- Once this information has been digested, set the class to work on photocopiable page 65.

REVIEW

- Go over any questions which posed a problem.

- If you have time, cover up the information on the board and run a quick-fire quiz about the facts about angles pupils should know.

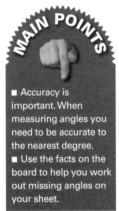
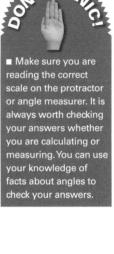

Angles

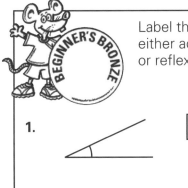

Label these angles as either acute, obtuse or reflex.

1. [ ]

2. [ ]

3. [ ]

4. [ ]

Use a protractor or angle measurer to measure these angles.

5. [ ]

6. [ ]

7. [ ]

Find the missing angles in these triangles.

8.
60°   65°

9.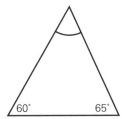
100°   43°

10. Draw an angle of 82° to the nearest degree.

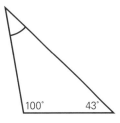

FREQUENCY TABLES

INTRODUCTION

■ The pupils should be familiar with simple pictograms and bar charts. Ask the class if they remember doing surveys and showing the data as a bar chart or pictogram. If they can't remember or don't know what they are, then start there with a Year 3 text book!

■ The area of Data Handling that causes most difficulty in SATs papers is interpreting graphs that represent frequency of events.

WHOLE CLASS TEACHING

■ Frequency tables need to be looked at carefully so you can understand what they are telling you.

■ Look at the table on the board. Talk through the features of the table with the pupils before having them answer the questions.

■ Once everyone is clear about how the table works and what it is telling them, have them answer the questions on photocopiable page 67.

■ Everyone should attempt the Go for Gold! section.

REVIEW

■ Go over the Beginner's Bronze and Steady Silver questions first and answer any queries.

■ Now talk through what the pupils should have done in the Go for Gold! section. Discuss the results – were there any similarities among the graphs the pupils produced?

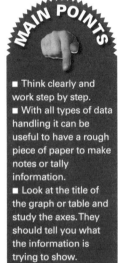

Frequency tables

This table shows the different ways Clara Loft 'died' during 'Pyramid Plunder' – a popular console game. Look at the table then answer the questions below.

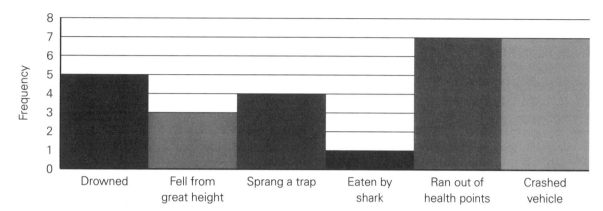

1. What was the least frequent cause of death? _____

2. How many times did Clara fall from a great height? _____

3. How many times in total did Clara crash a vehicle and spring a trap?

_____

4. How many games were played altogether? _____

5. Roll your dice 50 times. Tally the results in the chart. Draw a frequency bar chart like this one on a separate sheet of paper and use your results to complete the chart.

1	
2	
3	
4	
5	
6	

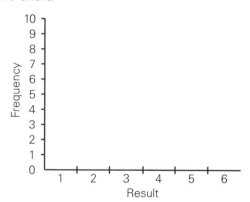

SCHOLASTIC
www.scholastic.co.uk

QUICK FIX FOR YEAR 6: **MATHS**

MULTI-STEP PROBLEMS

INTRODUCTION

■ Multi-step problems require you to think carefully (as always) and keep a note of each step you do.

■ You will need to choose and complete an operation, take the answer and do a further operation (possibly more) to that answer to get a final solution.

WHOLE CLASS TEACHING

■ Display the following problem on the board: 'Ivor Sorebum is cycling the 1086 miles from Land's End to John O'Groats. When he has cycled 150 miles, how far will it be until he is halfway?'

■ Work through the problem with the class and perform the calculations step by step, identifying the operations that need to be completed:

1. Halfway = 1086 ÷ 2 = 543 miles

2. Distance cycled = 150 miles

3. Difference between halfway and distance cycled = 543 – 150 = 393

4. The answer is: Ivor needs to cycle a further 393 miles before he is halfway.

■ Set the class to work on the rest of the problems (around the same topic) on photocopiable page 69.

REVIEW

■ Go over the problems with the class and provide the correct answers.

■ Inform the class that the 'solving problems' type of questions tend to be the most common in the SATs papers.

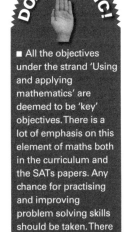

Multi-step problems

Answer these further questions about Ivor's cycle ride. Use a separate sheet for your working.

1. For the first 15 days, Ivor cycles 20 miles a day. After 15 days how much further has he got to go to complete his 1086 mile journey?

2. For the next 15 days, Ivor goes a bit faster and cycles 24 miles a day. How much further has he got to go now? (You need to have the correct answer to question 1!)

3. The remaining distance took Ivor just six days. He travelled the same distance on each of those days. How many more miles did Ivor travel on the last day of cycling than the first?

Now try these.

4. Ivor has a budget of £25 per day for food and accommodation. However, he only spent £22.50 per day over the trip which lasted 36 days. How much money did Ivor have left at the end of his journey?

5. During the ride, Ivor bought three spare tyres for £15.99 each. He also bought two puncture repair kits for £7.49 each. How much did he pay altogether?

6. Ivor carried 100 energy bars with him. He ate a fifth of them before reaching Glasgow, a quarter of the remainder by the time he reached Manchester and 26 on his way to Bristol. How many bars did Ivor have left for the remainder of his journey?

(calculator optional)

7. Ivor raised £6000 for his favourite charity. He put the money in the bank. The bank pays 7% interest per year. How much would the £6000 be worth after two years?

8. The bank manager tells Ivor that if he leaves the £6000 in for five years he will get a bonus payment of an additional 10% on the final balance. If he does this, how much will Ivor have in total after five years? (Round all pence UP/DOWN to the nearest pound.)

9. Ivor's next adventure was aiming to be the first person to reach the North Pole – on a Pogo stick! Remarkably, he made it and covered a distance of 2374 miles. His Mum sponsored him at 8p per mile and his Dad sponsored him for 13p per mile. (Everyone else thought he was mad!) How much did Ivor raise on his epic journey?

SCHOLASTIC
www.scholastic.co.uk

QUICK FIX FOR YEAR 6: MATHS

NUMBER PATTERNS

INTRODUCTION

■ Talk about number patterns which the class may be familiar with. When are the next Olympic Games? In what years will the next four Olympic Games be held?

■ Ask the class for another example (ideas include appearance of comets, years ending in '0', football World Cup).

WHOLE CLASS TEACHING

■ Explain to the class that they should always look for patterns in Maths. This is a skill which can save a great deal of time when dealing with lots of numbers.

■ Set the class to work on photocopiable page 71.

■ Early on, ask who has completed the first couple of questions. Whoever volunteers, ask them to tell everyone how they arrived at their answers. The key to answering this type of question (which they will get in the SATs) is finding the difference between the numbers you are given.

■ Once the class have been working for a few more minutes, do a couple of examples from the Silver section on the board. Ideally, you want all the pupils to be able to complete this section.

REVIEW

■ Review the answers and explain the sequences to anyone who is still unsure.

■ Reinforce the fact that finding the difference between the numbers you are given is key to identifying a number pattern.

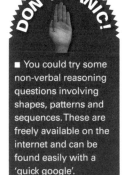

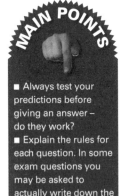

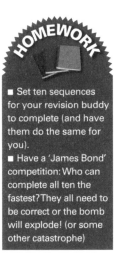

Number patterns

Write the next four numbers in each of these sequences.

1. 6, 16, _____

2. 20, 18, _____

3. 9, 109, _____

4. 0, 11, _____

5. 9, 16, _____

6. 40, 36, _____

Fill in the gaps in these sequences.

7. ☐ , ☐ 20, 25, 30, ☐

8. ☐ , ☐ 69, 59, ☐ , ☐ 29

9. 116, 120, 124, ☐ , ☐ , ☐ , ☐

10. 47, 56, ☐ , ☐ , 83, ☐ , ☐

11. 88, 94, ☐ , 106, ☐ , ☐

12. −18, −14, ☐ , −6, ☐ , ☐

Now try these questions.

13. The modern Summer Olympic Games were first held in 1896 and have been held every four years since. There have been three Games cancelled because of wars. How many Summer Olympics have there been up to the current year?

_____

_____

_____

14. Halley's Comet last appeared in 1986. It only appears every 76 years. When will the next five appearances be?

_____

_____

_____

QUICK FIX FOR YEAR 6: MATHS

END OF YEAR OBJECTIVES

Y5: Represent a puzzle or problem by identifying and recording the information or calculations needed to solve it; find possible solutions and confirm them in the context of the problem
Y6: Tabulate systematically the information in a problem or puzzle; identify and record the steps or calculations needed to solve it, using symbols where appropriate; interpret solutions in the original context and check their accuracy.
Explain reasoning and conclusions, using words, symbols or diagrams as appropriate

WHAT YOU NEED

■ Writing equipment
■ Rough paper
■ Photocopiable page 73 for each pupil

SOLVING PUZZLES

INTRODUCTION

■ Discuss the sort of puzzles the class will be trying to solve. Stress that they will be required to solve mathematical puzzles which could be about measures, shape, numbers and puzzles which are written in words but are about numbers!

■ As this is the last planned booster (you may have time to do more), aim for a session which allows the pupils to put their all-round maths skills into practice. You want them to have the confidence to try as many ways as possible to solve these puzzles and to perhaps think laterally or 'out of the box'.

WHOLE CLASS TEACHING

■ Set the class to work on photocopiable page 73.

■ During this lesson work individually with as many of the group as possible, offering support where needed. Take the chance to explore the mathematical thinking of each member of the class. Ask them to explain their methods and how they arrived at their answers.

REVIEW

Here are some questions to ask before, during and after the lesson.

■ What could you try next?

■ Is it a reasonable answer? What makes you so sure?

■ If you were doing this again, is there anything you would do differently?

■ What have you learned or found out today?

■ Have you learned any new mathematical vocabulary?

You could emphasise to the class that if they have understood and grasped all the concepts covered in the booster lessons (i.e. successfully completed up to Steady Silver at least on all the worksheets), then they are well on the way to scoring a Level 4 or above in their SATs.

MAIN POINTS

■ Work methodically step by step.
■ Use rough paper to make notes, draw diagrams or tables and organise your thinking in any way you find useful.
■ Look for patterns and rules and test them when you think you've found one that works.

DON'T PANIC!

■ If you really get stuck on a puzzle, don't give up! It can sometimes help if you go away and do something entirely different. You might come back to the problem, view it from a different angle and come up with a new idea or even go straight to the solution.

HOMEWORK

■ Review all 20 lessons and highlight any areas of weakness. There should still be time to address these by further practice and input from your teachers and teaching assistants.

Solving puzzles

Try these to warm up. Use a separate sheet for your working.

1. I am a two-digit number that is odd. If you turn me upside down I become smaller but even. Who am I? _____

2. Can you find three numbers that have the same answer when multiplied together as when they are added together? _____

3. There are 100 houses built along Einstein Crescent. Albert the signmaker needs to number the houses from 1 to 100. How many '9' digits will he need? _____

4. If MATHEMATICS is 82490824631 in Jane's code, what is:

a) CATS _____   **b)** MICE _____   **c)** CHEESE _____

5. If $1\frac{1}{2}$ dozen eggs cost £1.80, how much do 18 eggs cost?

_____

6. In a three-team football tournament, each team played once against each of the other teams. They scored 2 points for a win and 1 point for a draw (no points for a loss). Each team only scored one goal.
The final results were:
Rovers – 3 points
United – 2 points
Rangers – 1 point
What was the score in each match?

Match	Score
Rovers v United	
Rovers v Rangers	
United v Rangers	

7. Leo makes the following statement: 'The day before yesterday I was 11 years old and next year I will turn 14.'

When is Leo's birthday? _____

8. How many squares can you find in this shape?

_____

MENTAL MATHS WARM-UP GAMES

Before each booster lesson you may wish to warm-up the class with some mental arithmetic. There may not always be time as you will need to complete the booster lesson and there may be restrictions over the use of a classroom at lunchtime or other such problems. However, the game described below is a good game to play at any time of the day, and it can be played for as long as you wish.

MATHEMATICAL MASTERMIND

This is a fast-moving, teacher-led game. The more enthusiasm and 'showmanship' the teacher puts in, the better the response from the pupils – so go for it!

■ All the children are given three 'lives' which they 'keep in their head'.

■ The teacher asks a quick fire question such as 'Double 26' or 'What's the product of 8 and 9?'

■ First hand up gets to answer but they must answer straight away. Any hesitation and a life is lost.

■ A correct answer immediately gains a life.

■ Stop the game after a few questions and ask 'Who has 2 lives?', 'Who has 3 lives?' etc.

■ Vary the questions so you cover all mathematical areas, including shape, angles and measures, e.g. 'I'm 2-D and have three sides, what am I?' or 'How many degrees in a whole turn?'.

■ Trick questions are allowed!

■ Stop when you have a winner (the last pupil with one or more lives left), or when time runs out. If you have a tie, then ask a tie-breaker question. This should be something that is unusual; maybe where the pupils have to get closest to the answer. A bit of teacher knowledge is useful here so arm yourself with a few number facts. For example:

  ■ How high in feet is Mount Everest? (29 028)

  ■ How many days did it take Ellen McArthur to sail around the world single-handed? (71 days and 14 hours)

  ■ Roughly how far away is the sun? (93 million miles/149 600 000km)

  ■ How many seats are there at Brighton and Hove Albion's football ground? (7000)

  ■ How old was the oldest living person when they died? (122 years and 164 days – Jeanne Calment of France (1875–1997). Jeanne met Vincent Van Gogh when she was 14!)

DARTS

Playing darts is a terrific way to improve and practise mental maths skills as well as hand/eye coordination. It requires adding, subtracting, doubling, trebling and multiplying skills, to be performed quickly and correctly. Buy one of those 'safe' magnetic dartboards for use in the classroom, during wet breaktimes. Make sure the dartboard doesn't have an automatic scoring device!

PICK A NUMBER

Ask a volunteer to pick any two-digit number (e.g. 42). Write the number in large digits on the board. Now ask the class questions around that number. For example:

■ What is 42 doubled?

■ What is 42 halved?

■ What is 42 multiplied by 3?

■ How many 7s make 42?

■ Is 42 divisible by 3?

Move on to three-digit numbers if need be.

MENTAL BINGO!

This requires a bit of preparation but once you have made a set of bingo cards, they can be used many times.

You need:

■ A4 'bingo' cards made by dividing a piece of card into a 16-rectangle grid. In each rectangle write the answer to a sum, the name of a shape, a time or a mathematical term. Vary the answers as much as possible.

■ A stack of small cards with the questions written on. These must match the answers on the A4 'bingo' cards.

■ Give each pupil a bingo card or divide the class into teams, with a bingo card for each team.

■ Draw out the questions from a bag, tin or box.

■ Call out the questions in a theatrical way!

■ The pupils place a counter or multi-link cube over any answers which match the questions.

■ The first person or team to make a line of four, or match all four corners calls out 'Mental Bingo!' (or something similar).

EXPECTATIONS FOR MENTAL CALCULATION

These are the expectations for mental calculation in Years 5 and 6. You could refer to these before playing Mathematical Mastermind or when setting any mental arithmetic task. You could also photocopy this and give a copy to each pupil as a checklist of skills.

Year 5	
Rapid recall	Children should be able to recall rapidly: multiplication facts up to 10 x 10 and division facts corresponding to tables up to 10 x 10
Mental strategies	Children should be able to use the following strategies for mental calculations: ■ Count up through the next multiple of 10, 100 or 1000 ■ Reorder numbers in a calculation ■ Partition into hundreds, tens and units, adding the most significant digit first ■ Use known number facts and place value to add or subtract pairs of three-digit multiples of 10 and two-digit numbers with one decimal place ■ Add or subtract the nearest multiple of 10 or 100 then adjust ■ Identify near-doubles ■ Add several numbers ■ Use the relationship between addition and subtraction ■ Use factors ■ Partition to carry out multiplication ■ Use doubling and halving ■ Use closely related facts to carry out multiplication and division ■ Use the relationship between multiplication and division ■ Use knowledge of number facts and place value to multiply or divide
Mental calculations	Children should be able to carry out the following calculations mentally: ■ Add or subtract any pair of three-digit multiples of 10 ■ Find what must be added to a decimal with units and tenths to make the next highest whole number ■ Add or subtract any pair of decimal fractions each with units and tenths or each with tenths and hundredths. ■ Subtract a four-digit number just less than a multiple of 1000 from a four-digit number just more than a multiple of 1000 ■ Multiply any two- or three-digit number by 10 or 100 ■ Multiply any two-digit number multiple of 10 by a single digit. ■ Double any whole number from 1 to 100 and multiples of 10 to 1000, and find corresponding halves ■ Find 50%, 25% and 10% of a small whole number or quantity

Year 6	
Rapid recall	In addition to the skills required in Year 5, children should be able to recall: the squares of all the whole numbers from 1 to 10
Mental strategies	As well as all strategies from previous years, children should be able to use the following strategies for mental calculations: ■ Use knowledge of number facts and place value to add or subtract pairs of three-digit multiples of 10 and two-digit numbers with one decimal place ■ Add or subtract the nearest multiple of 10, 100 or 1000 then adjust
Mental calculations	Children should be able to mentally: ■ Multiply any two-digit number by a single digit ■ Multiply any two-digit number by 50 or 25 ■ Multiply or divide any whole number by 10 or 100, giving any remainder as a decimal ■ Find squares of multiples of 10 to 100 ■ Find any multiple of 10% of a whole number or quantity

MENTAL MATHS TEST

- Each pupil will need a copy of the answer sheet on page 79.
- Read each question twice.
- Pupils can make notes but they don't have to.
- Each question is worth 1 mark.
- Allow the correct amount of time for each question.

QUESTIONS

Say to the class: *I will now start the test. I shall read each question twice. For the first group of questions, you have five seconds to work out each answer and write it on your sheet.*

SECTION 1

1. How many 20p pieces are there in £3?
2. Take away 60 from 130.
3. What is the product of 7 and 8?
4. How would quarter to nine in the morning be shown on a 24-hour clock?
5. How many centimetres are there in $2\frac{1}{2}$ metres?

SECTION 2

Say to the class: *For the next set of questions, you have ten seconds to work out each answer and write it on your sheet.*

6. Dennis buys a comic for 70p and pays with a £5 note. How much change does he get?
7. What is double 530?
8. A train is due at 3.45. It is 25 minutes late. At what time does it arrive?
9. A square courtyard has a perimeter of 100m. What is the length of one of its sides?
10. What is the total of 4.2 and 6.9?
11. Picture a square-based pyramid. How many faces does it have?
12. What is the next number in this sequence? 18, 36, 54, …
13. Write a fraction which is equivalent to 75%.
14. What is the difference between 427 and 856?
15. What is 5.5 multiplied by 100?

SECTION 3

Say to the class: *For the next set of questions, you have 15 seconds to work out each answer and write it on your sheet.*

16. Add 52, 77 and 39.
17. In a sale there is 50% off all prices. A snooker table is priced at £35. How much was it before the sale?
18. What number is halfway between 36 and 80?
19. Out of 100 pet owners, 68% preferred dogs and the rest liked cats. How many of the pet owners liked cats?
20. Two internal angles of a triangle measure 48 degrees and 62 degrees. What is the size of the third internal angle?

Say to the class: *Put your pencils down, the test has finished.*

MENTAL MATHS PUPIL ANSWER SHEET

SECTION 1

For this group of questions, you have 5 seconds to work out each answer and write it on your sheet.

1.	How many 20p pieces are there in £3?
2.	Take away 60 from 130.
3.	What is the product of 7 and 8?
4.	How would quarter to nine in the morning be shown on a 24-hour clock?
5.	How many centimetres are there in $2\frac{1}{2}$ metres?

SECTION 2

For this set of questions, you have 10 seconds to work out each answer and write it on your sheet.

6.	Dennis buys a comic for 70p and pays with a £5 note. How much change does he get?
7.	What is double 530?
8.	A train is due at 3.45. It is 25 minutes late. At what time does it arrive?
9.	A square courtyard has a perimeter of 100m. What is the length of one of its sides?
10.	What is the total of 4.2 and 6.9?
11.	Picture a square-based pyramid. How many faces does it have?
12.	What is the next number in this sequence? 18, 36, 54, …
13.	Write a fraction which is equivalent to 75%.
14.	What is the difference between 427 and 856?
15.	What is 5.5 multiplied by 100?

SECTION 3

For this set of questions, you have 15 seconds to work out each answer and write it on your sheet.

16.	Add 52, 77 and 39.
17.	In a sale there is 50% off all prices. A snooker table is priced at £35. How much was it before the sale?
18.	What number is halfway between 36 and 80?
19.	Out of 100 pet owners, 68% preferred dogs and the rest liked cats. How many of the pet owners liked cats?
20.	Two internal angles of a triangle measure 48 degrees and 62 degrees. What is the size of the third internal angle?

Total out of 20 [ ]

■SCHOLASTIC
www.scholastic.co.uk

QUICK FIX FOR YEAR 6: MATHS

ACTIVITIES FOR GIFTED AND TALENTED CHILDREN

The Government deems the top 5% of children in this country to be 'gifted and talented'. Generally speaking, the 'gifted tag' is aimed at the core subjects and the 'talented' tag at sports and arts. Schools need to be seen to provide for these pupils throughout the curriculum.

Over the next three pages there are maths activities which should cater for this group and also provide some of your average to high ability children with a healthy challenge (see also activity below). Some of the activities require items of equipment, but nothing you won't find in the average classroom. Others take the form of problems which require lateral thinking and challenge the pupils to use a less conventional approach to the problem. There are problems which test logic, intelligence and thinking skills – all useful areas to develop in the primary school child as well as adults!

You could group the children in mixed-ability tables if you wish to use the activities with the whole class. Some of the questions only require discussion, so there should be an opportunity for everyone to contribute.

There are hints for some of the problems (upside down at the bottom of the page) – children should only use these if they are well and truly stuck.

DIABOLICAL DATES

a) A month begins on a Friday and ends on a Friday as well. What month is it?
b) If I add the date of the last Monday of this month and the date of the first Monday of next month, I get 38. Both dates are in the same year. What is the current month?

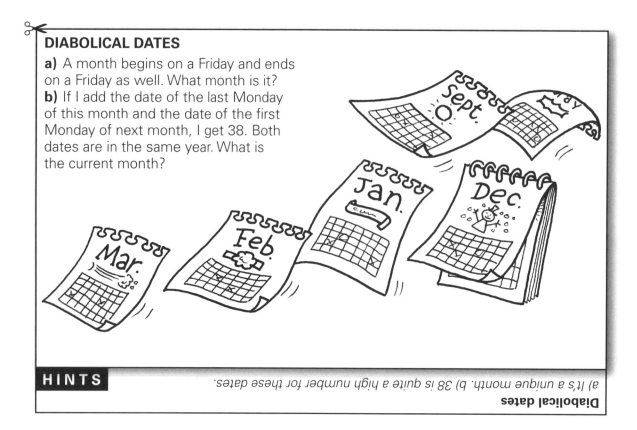

HINTS

Diabolical dates
a) It's a unique month. b) 38 is quite a high number for these dates.

CONNIE'S CON TRICK

Connie Conster the notorious con-artist has a new con. She places 40 matches on a table and tells Simple Simon he can take 1, 3 or 5 matches each time. The winner is the one who takes the last match. Simon goes first and takes 3 matches. Who wins the game and why?

HINTS

Connie's con trick

Remember, each player takes an odd number each time.

THE TIDE IS HIGH

A boat is anchored offshore. In order for the crew to reach the rowing boat, they have to go down a 22-step ladder. Each step is 12cm high. The tide rises at a rate of 6cm per hour. How many steps will the tide have covered after 10 hours?

AROUND THE WORLD

Sir Francis Drake was the first person to sail around the world in his ship the *Golden Hind*. When he got back, his navigator asked him this question: 'What part of the *Golden Hind* travelled the longest distance?'
Sir Francis didn't have a clue.
Do you?

TRIANGLE TROUBLE

You need six toothpicks or matches of equal length.

Your task is to make four equilateral triangles using six toothpicks of equal length.

HINTS

Triangle trouble
Think 3-D.

IN MY PRIME

Find three different two-digit prime numbers where the average of all three is prime and the average of any two is prime.

BAR HUMBUG!

Fingers Finley has stolen a gold bar measuring 40cm. He wants to post it back to his hideout to avoid suspicion. However, the maximum length for posting such packages is 30cm. How does Fingers successfully post the gold bar without changing its shape in any way?

HINTS

Bar humbug!
Think 'inside the box'!

PENNIES FROM HEAVEN

Great Aunt Eliza has gathered the family around her bed – she is very sick. She says, 'I will leave my fortune to the one who can collect the exact number of pennies equalling half the number of days that I have left to live.' What would you do to inherit the fortune?

FASTER THAN THE SPEED OF LIGHT?

George Lard (he's a big chap) claims he can switch his bedroom light off and get into bed before the room is dark. The light switch and bed are 6m apart. Last week he proved he could do it. How is it possible?

LOSER'S CHESS

This is a fast and fun game which requires a standard chess board and pieces and knowledge of the rules of chess.

The object is to lose all of your pieces, king included, or be stalemated (unable to play a move).

Ignore checks and checkmates.

Players must capture a piece where they can, but when there is a choice of pieces that can be taken they can choose.

All the other rules are the same as in ordinary chess.

ANSWERS

LEVEL 3 SAMPLE TEST

1. **a)** 4 **b)** 3

2. 15, 35 and 40

3. 21 and 59

4. **a)** 4 **b)** 3

5. $\frac{1}{3} = \frac{2}{6}$

6. **a)** –4°C **b)** –7°C **c)** 3

7. **a)** 57, 61, 75, 86, 93, 104 **b)** 47 **c)** 112

8. **a)** Finley 50, Jamie 35, Stephanie 45, Scarlett 15

   b)

9. **a)**

   b)

   c)

10. **a)** $\frac{1}{4}$ **b)** $\frac{2}{8}$

11. 8

12.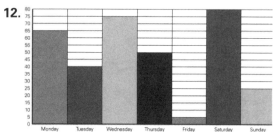

13. sphere   cone   cuboid   cylinder
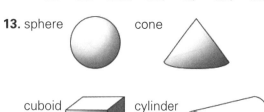

triangular-based pyramid

triangular prism

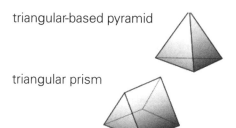

14. **a)** 8 pounds, 65 pence
    b) 10 pounds, 54 pence
    c) 109 pounds, 31 pence
    d) 287 pounds, 90 pence

15. **a)** Weight: large rock – kg; tree trunk – kg; pine cone – g; worm – g
    b) Length: spider – cm; height of a tree – m; leaf – cm; bridge – m
    c) Capacity: pond – l; jam-jar – ml; teaspoon – ml; bucket – l

LEVEL 4 SAMPLE TEST

1. **a)** $\underline{500} \div 10 = 5\underline{0}$ **b)** $\underline{80} \times 10 = \underline{800}$

2. **a)** Sample answer: $\underline{45} \div \underline{5} = 9$
   b) $\underline{17} \times \underline{3} = 51$ or $\underline{3} \times \underline{17} = 51$ or $\underline{1} \times \underline{51} = 51$ or $\underline{51} \times \underline{1} = 51$

3. **a)** 137 **b)** 448

4. Less than half: $\frac{1}{10}, \frac{5}{12}, \frac{2}{5}, \frac{2}{9}$.
   Half: $\frac{1}{2}, \frac{9}{18}, \frac{3}{6}$. More than half: $\frac{4}{7}, \frac{3}{4}, \frac{2}{3}$.

5. Less than half: 25%, 33%, 48%, 7%. Half: 50%. More than half: 61%, 74%.

6. Less than half: 0.33, 0.25, 0.05. Half: 0.5. More than half: 0.6, 1.65, 1.5

7. $\frac{1}{8}$

8. 0.86m

9. Andy should buy the racket from the department store because it is £15 cheaper.

10. 12.12pm

11. Finishing order: Ricky, Debbie, Charlotte, Jordan, Raj, Zac, Meg, Lihan

12. **a)**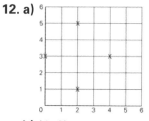

    b) (4, 3)

13. a)

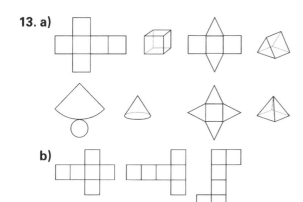

b)

14.

Shape	All angles are right angles	All sides equal in length	Opposite sides are parallel
A	✓	✗	✓
B			
C	✓	✓	✓
D			✓
E			
F	✓	✓	✓

15. 34 and 43

16. 18

17. (72p ÷ 2) x 5 = £1.80

18. Katie was 29 away from the correct answer and Chantelle was 26 away from the correct answer so Chantelle was closer by 3.

19. a) Pravin would have £2.25 left over.
b) Courtney spent the remaining £2 on the Helter-Skelter (£1.25) and in the Hall of Mirrors (75p).

LESSON PHOTOCOPIABLES
PLACE VALUE

1. 865

2. 235

3. 863

4. 236

5. 9741: Nine thousand seven hundred and forty-one

6. 1047: One thousand and forty-seven

7. 9714: Nine thousand seven hundred and fourteen

8. 1079: One thousand and seventy-nine

9. 97 x 53 + 10 = 5151

ORDERING DECIMALS

Bronze

Stanley – 4.1m; Harry – 3.8m; Grace – 3.6m; Mehmet – 3.2m; Mary – 2.5m; Rochelle – 2.1m; Billy – 1.7m

Silver

Grace – 20.31m; Billy – 19.47m; Isabella – 18.2m; Harry – 15.5m; Melissa – 13.75m; Mehmet – 13.52m; Mary – 13.25m

Gold

Crawford – 9.909s; Wells – 9.995s; Christie – 10.003s; Thompson – 10.061s; Lewis – 10.318s; Greene – 10.381s

A WRITTEN METHOD FOR ADDITION

1. 141

2. 253

3. 158

4. 395

5. 1859

6. 1447

7. 2492

8. 1447

9. 1448

10. 12 748

11. 14 795

12. 16 110

13. 86.2

14. 122.23

15. 168.04

A WRITTEN METHOD FOR SUBTRACTION

1. 44

2. 35

3. 35

4. 42

5. 91

6. 515

7. 316

8. 407

9. 209

10. 5507

11. 459

12. 6276

13. 2.62

14. 4.95

15. 21.16

A WRITTEN METHOD FOR MULTIPLICATION

1. 256

2. 504

3. 205

4. 384

5. 1581

6. 4180

7. 2555

8. 5628

9. 2242

10. 18 126

11. 45 144

12. 33.6

13. 218.4

14. 135.6

15. 42.14

A WRITTEN METHOD FOR DIVISION

1. 7

2. 7 r 3

3. 17 r 3

4. 18

5. 22

6. 20

7. 20

8. 26

9. 116

10. 94

11. 78 r 2

12. 98 r 2

13. 18

14. 23

15. 37

16. 33

17. 56

18. 99

USING A CALCULATOR

1. 1034

2. 366

3. 3388

4. 145

5. 80.25

6. 17 977.6

7. 10 100

8. 68.9

9. 2

10. −9

11. 71.495

12. 281

13. £586.79

CHECKING YOUR ANSWERS

1. 357: Check 357 + 67 = 424

2. 42: Check 42 x 4 = 168

3. 438: Check 438 − 42 = 396

4. 225: Check 225 ÷ 3 = 75

5. 8657: Rough answer 800 x 10 = 8000

6. 269: Rough answer 400 − 100 = 300

7. 28: Rough answer 500 ÷ 20 = 25

8. 873: Rough answer 500 + 400 = 900

9. Correct

10. Wrong – correct answer 675

11. Correct

12. Correct

13. Wrong – correct answer 15,477

14. Correct

15. Wrong – correct answer 111,776

16. Correct

FRACTIONS AND PERCENTAGES OF QUANTITIES

1. 60p

2. £6

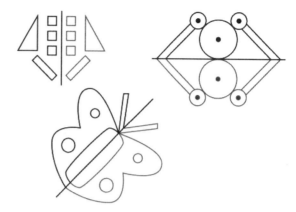

3. £1.50

4. £6

5. 50kg

6. 4.5 litres

7. 200m

8. 45 (minutes)

9. $\frac{3}{8}$

10. $\frac{3}{10}$

11. $\frac{1}{6}$

12. The Kaiser Chefs (8 out of 40 = 20%)

FACTORS, MULTIPLES AND PRIMES

1. 1, 2, 4, 8, 16

2. 1, 2, 4, 5, 10, 20

3. 1, 2, 4, 8, 16, 32

4. 1, 2, 4, 5, 10, 20, 50, 100

5. 2, 3, 5, 7, 11, 13, 17, 19, 23, 29, 31, 37, 41, 43, 47, 53, 59, 61, 67, 71, 73, 79, 83, 89, 97

COORDINATES IN THE FIRST QUADRANT

1. Skull Rock

2. (10, 2)

3. (14, 1)

4. (11, 11), (11, 12), (13, 11), (13, 12)

5. Port Spain to Jelly-fish Beach

6. A triangle

7. Various answers but (6, 14) and (10, 10) is one possible pair.

REFLECTIVE SYMMETRY

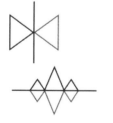

DRAWING AND MEASURING LINES

1. 5.0cm

2. 3.0cm

3. 1.5cm

4. 7.0cm

Nos 5 – 7 need to be drawn to the exact millimetre.

8. 100m

9. 101mm

10. 103mm

11. 107.5mm

PERIMETER

1. 12cm

2. 18cm

3. 15cm

4. 24cm

5. 90cm

6. 98m

7. 22.2m

FINDING THE AREA OF RECTANGLES

1. 8cm²

2. 4cm²

3. 14cm²

4. 84cm²

5. 96cm²

6. 240cm²

7. 1574cm²

8. 625m² (check they have put m not cm!)

9. 189cm²

ANGLES

1. acute

2. acute

3. obtuse

4. reflex

5. 45°

6. 110°

7. 230°

8. 55°

9. 37°

FREQUENCY TABLES

1. Being eaten by a shark

2. 3

3. 11

4. 27

MULTI-STEP PROBLEMS

1. 786 miles

2. 426 miles

3. 51 miles

4. £90

5. £62.95

6. 34 bars

7. £6869.40

8. £9258

9. £498.54

NUMBER PATTERNS

1. 26, 36, 46, 56

2. 16, 14, 12, 10

3. 209, 309, 409, 509

4. 22, 33, 44, 55

5. 23, 30, 37, 44

6. 32, 28, 24, 20

7. <u>10</u>, <u>15</u>, 20, 25, 30, <u>35</u>

8. <u>89</u>, <u>79</u>, 69, 59, <u>49</u>, <u>39</u>, 29

9. 116, 120, 124, <u>128</u>, <u>132</u>, <u>136</u>, <u>140</u>

10. 47, 56, <u>65</u>, <u>74</u>, 83, <u>92</u>, <u>101</u>

11. 88, 94, <u>100</u>, 106, <u>112</u>, <u>118</u>

12. –18, –14, <u>–10</u>, –6, <u>–2</u>, 2

13. Up to 2007 there have been 25 Summer Olympics.

14. 2062, 2138, 2214, 2290 and 2366

SOLVING PUZZLES

1. 99 (66)

2. 1, 2 and 3 (1 + 2 + 3 = 6; 1 x 2 x 3 = 6)

3. 20

4. a) 3241   **b)** 8630   **c)** 390010

5. £1.80

6. Rovers 0 United 0; Rovers 1 Rangers 0; United 1 Rangers 1: Rovers could only get three points by drawing one match and winning the other. Since they only scored one goal, the results must be 1 – 0 and 0 – 0. Rangers drew one and lost the other match. The scores must have been 1 – 1 and 0 – 1. Their drawn game must have been against United. So, Rovers beat Rangers 1 – 0 and drew with United 0 – 0.

7. Leo's birthday is; December 31st – he was talking on January 1st. He is 12 now; the day before yesterday he was 11; on December 31st this calendar year he will turn 13; and next calendar year he will turn 14.

8. There are 14 squares.

MENTAL MATHS TEST

1. 15

2. 70

3. 56

4. 08:45

5. 250

6. £4.30

7. 1060

8. 4:10

9. 25m

10. 11.1

11. 5

12. 72

13. $\frac{3}{4}$

14. 429

15. 550

16. 168
17. £70
18. 58
19. 32
20. 70°

ACTIVITIES FOR GIFTED AND TALENTED CHILDREN
DIABOLICAL DATES

a) February of a leap year. If a month starts and ends with the same day of the week, it must have a complete number of weeks plus an extra day.

b) The current month is July. To add up to 38, it can only be the highest possible number for the last Monday of the month (31) and the highest for the first Monday of the next month (7). Therefore, both this month and the next month have to have 31 days. July and August are the only consecutive 31-day months in any calendar year.

CONNIE'S CON TRICK

Connie wins! Each player takes an odd number of matches each turn. After the first player goes, there will always be an odd number of matches left. After the second player goes, there will always be an even number of matches left – so the player who goes second will always win.

THE TIDE IS HIGH

The tide will not have covered any steps. The ship floats and will rise with the tide.

AROUND THE WORLD

The highest point (the top of the tallest mast) of the *Golden Hind* will have travelled the furthest distance. ($2\pi d$ longer than the lowest point of the ship which is d metres lower.)

TRIANGLE TROUBLE

It is impossible to make four equilateral triangles in a 2-D way – you can do it by making a 3-D tetrahedron (a regular triangular pyramid).

BAR HUMBUG!

Fingers Finley can post the bar in a box which measures 30cm x 30cm. It will fit diagonally.

IN MY PRIME

11, 47 and 71

PENNIES FROM HEAVEN

You will have the exact amount if you save a penny every other day until she dies.

FASTER THAN THE SPEED OF LIGHT?

George switches the light off during the day while it is still light.

KEY MATHS FACTS

Learning these key facts will provide a good grounding for success in the national tests. They should be looked at daily and time to spend learning them should be integrated into every pupil's revision timetable.

NUMBER AND CALCULATION

Multiplying decimals by 10, 100 and 1000

- Shuffle digits to the left of the decimal point.
- Shuffle once when x 10, twice when x 100 and three times when x 1000.

Dividing decimals by 10, 100 and 1000

- Shuffle digits to the right of the decimal point.
- Shuffle once when ÷ 10, twice when ÷ 100 and three times when ÷ 1000.

Negative numbers

- 'Integer' is a term meaning 'whole number'.
- When counting from negative up to positive or positive down to negative, remember to count the zero.
- When counting on a horizontal number line, count to the right when adding and to the left when subtracting.

Decimals to two places

- When rounding, remember 5 rounds up – for example, 4.285 = 4.29 to 2 d.p.
- Add the zero if needed when ordering or calculating decimals. It helps to avoid mistakes – for example, 56.3 = 56.30

Reducing a fraction to its lowest form

- To reduce a fraction to its simplest form, find a common factor which you can divide into the numerator and the denominator. For example, 4 ÷ 12: 4 divides into 4 once and into 12 three times, so $4 \div 12 = \frac{1}{3}$.

Calculating a fraction, decimal or percentage

- Learn as many fraction, decimal and percentage equivalents as you can. Certainly all of these:

$1 = 1.0 = 100\%$	$\frac{1}{5} = 0.20 = 20\%$
$\frac{1}{2} = 0.5 = 50\%$	$\frac{1}{10} = 0.10 = 10\%$
$\frac{1}{4} = 0.25 = 25\%$	$\frac{1}{100} = 0.01 = 1\%$
$\frac{3}{4} = 0.75 = 75\%$	$\frac{1}{3} = $ nearly $0.33 = $ nearly 33%

SCHOLASTIC
www.scholastic.co.uk

Multiplication and division (with decimal points)

- Multiplication and division are inverse operations (opposites).
- Always estimate an answer first. It will help you get the decimal point in the right place if you have removed it to make the calculation easier.

Calculating

- Remember – **Estimate, Calculate, Check!**
- Learn the column methods for the four operations.
- Familiarise yourself with using a pocket calculator.
- Always do calculations in brackets first.
- Learn all the multiplication facts up to 10 x 10 and be able to recall them instantly.

Checking your answers

- Check addition by subtraction – and vice versa.
- Check division by multiplication – and vice versa.
- Use friendly numbers when estimating: 2, 5, 10 and 100.

Simple formulae

- Talk through the formula in your mind. It will make it easier to understand and to remember.

Coordinates

- Always read ALONG the x axis, then UP or DOWN the y axis.
- Always write coordinates in brackets with the x coordinate before the y coordinate.
- Quadrants work anti-clockwise:

$$\begin{array}{c|c} 2 & 1 \\ \hline 3 & 4 \end{array}$$

SHAPE AND MEASURES

2-D shapes

- Parallelogram – a parallelogram is a rectangle that has been pushed over.

■ Rhombus – a rhombus is a square that has been pushed over.

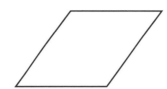

■ Trapezium – a trapezium has one pair of parallel lines.

■ Kite – kites have two pairs of sides next to each other which are equal in length but not parallel.

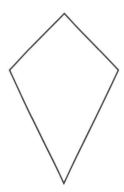

■ Equilateral triangles have three sides of equal length and three equal internal angles.

■ Isosceles triangles have two sides of equal length and two equal angles.

■ Scalene triangles have three sides of different lengths and all three internal angles are different.

■ Right-angled triangles have one angle which is a right angle.

Angles

■ Acute angle = 0–89 degrees

■ Right angle = 90 degrees

■ Obtuse angle = 91–179 degrees

■ Straight line = 180 degrees

■ Reflex angle = 181–359 degrees

■ Angles around a point add up to 360 degrees (one complete turn).

■ The internal angles of a triangle always add up to 180 degrees.

Symmetry

■ When drawing reflections, remember to keep the correct distance from the mirror line.

Some metric and Imperial conversions (approximate)

■ 1 litre ≈ 1.8 pints
■ 1 kilogram ≈ 2.2lbs (pounds)
■ 1 pound ≈ 0.454kg
■ 1 mile ≈ 1.6km
■ 5 miles ≈ 8km
■ 1 foot ≈ 30cm
■ 1 metre ≈ 3 feet 3 inches
■ 1 inch ≈ 2.5cm

Estimating measures

■ 'Milli' = very small
■ 'Centi' = small
■ 'Kilo' = large

Area of a rectangle

■ The formula for finding the area of a rectangle is *length* x *breadth* (*l* x *b*).
■ Area is always measured in units squared (mm^2, cm^2, m^2).

HANDLING DATA

Pictograms

■ Remember: picture = number; half a picture = half the number.

Charts and graphs

■ Be careful and accurate.
■ Read what the chart or graph is telling you.
■ Use a sharp pencil.
■ Pie charts are good for showing fractions, decimals and percentages.

EXAM TECHNIQUES – HINTS AND TIPS

BEFORE A TEST...

- When you revise, try revising 'little and often' rather than in long chunks. This is far more productive!
- Revise with your 'revision buddy' whenever possible. You can learn from each other, spot each other's mistakes and 'test' each other.
- Make sure you are up to speed with your recall of the multiplication facts up to 10 x 10.
- Get a good night's sleep before taking a test.
- Get up in good time and eat a good breakfast (a banana makes a 'brain-friendly' snack).
- Be prepared – wear a watch so you can tell the time during your test.

DURING A TEST...

- Don't rush. Read each question twice and be clear about what you being asked to do.
- If you get stuck, don't linger too long on the same question; you can always come back to it later.
- Never leave a multiple-choice question unanswered – make a good guess at the end.
- Check to see how many marks each question is worth. Has your answer merited those marks?
- Always check your answers. Do they 'look' correct?
- Keep an eye on the time. After 20 minutes, see how far you have got.
- Leave four to five minutes at the end to go through your work. You may spot a silly mistake. Try not to leave any questions unanswered. If you really can't get the answer, then make an educated guess. Use your estimating skills!
- Always show your method or 'working out'. It may be worth a mark, even if your answer is wrong.
- Double check any calculations you do with a calculator.
- Finally, don't get stressed. Think of the test as being given the chance to show what you know.

KEY FACTS ABOUT THE SATS

- The tests take place at your school but are marked by examiners – not your teacher.
- You will get the results in July.
- Individual scores are not made public but a school's overall scores are published in what are commonly known as the 'league tables'.
- Your results will not affect your application or entry into secondary school.

REWARDS AND MOTIVATION

All children (and adults!) respond well to praise and encouragement. Talk about class/year group rewards for when the SATs are over and for individual attendance and achievement in the booster classes.

This is to certify that

_____

has attended _____ booster classes
(insert number)

at _____ School

and attained a

BRONZE / SILVER / GOLD medal

Signed _____ *Year 6 class teacher*

Signed _____ *Headteacher*

Date _____

QUICK FIX FOR YEAR 6: MATHS

In this series:

ISBN 978-0439-94569-1

ISBN 978-0439-94568-4

ISBN 978-0439-94513-4

ISBN 978-0439-94512-7

To find out more, call: 0845 603 9091
or visit our website www.scholastic.co.uk